Lowell School

A SINGING SCHOOL

OUR FIRST MUSIC

Editors

THERESA ARMITAGE
PETER W. DYKEMA
GLADYS PITCHER
FLOY ADELE ROSSMAN
J. LILIAN VANDEVERE

Advisory Editors

CHARLES H. FARNSWORTH
HERMAN F. SMITH

Art Editor

MARTHA POWELL SETCHELL

CALIFORNIA STATE SERIES

Published by California State Department of Education

Sacramento · 1942

California State Printing Office

Sacramento

1ED.   6M   1942

11 - 41

Our First Music

INTRODUCTION

THE PLAN of this book is based on the idea that music can and should strengthen the general educational aims in the primary grades. In later years of the child's life music may be subdivided into separated aspects, but in his early school years not only are its various phases grouped by the child under the single idea of music, but all of its various manifestations are closely related to the rest of the child's life.

Our musical material is presented in units of study, the unifying idea of each being a topic which is commonly found in first grade courses of study.

But neither the order of presentation nor the subject matter of the topics should be considered as either fixed or obligatory. The teacher should feel free to choose the sequence and content of her presentation of material. To facilitate this flexibility of choice, references are frequently given in one unit to related material in other units. Moreover, all the material in the book is combined in a general index which contains not only all the topics for interrelations suggested in the individual units, but many additional ones. The teacher, therefore, has available a large variety of material to meet practically every situation in which music can be advantageously used.

All of the musical material is presented in such form that it may be played on the piano. Many of the piano versions are not beyond Grades 2 and 3 of the commonly accepted sevenfold classification of piano material, but some involve passages of a little greater difficulty. The songs are usually effective with melody only but for the instrumental pieces this will seldom suffice. Suitable phonograph records may replace the piano, especially with the music given for listening, rhythmic expression, and rhythm band.

Sharing Summer Experiences

I. Guiding Educational Principles

AT THE OPENING OF the school year, to aid each child to gain confidence in himself in the new and strange school group, and to extend his acquaintance with his school mates, happy summer experiences may profitably be recalled. In spite of the great variety of the experiences of the children there will always be certain activities and certain emotions which all have shared and which will thus hold the interest of the entire group.

This condition is the justification for using "Sharing Summer Experiences" as the first unifying topic. Many of these experiences were doubtless related to music and some of them can easily be expressed in music suitable for the group. All normal children enjoy music in some of its various forms and the introducing of musical activities into each day's program helps greatly in making the school a happy place. Under its warming influence, the child reveals his interests and thus helps the teacher to understand his needs. She may thus begin, on the very first day, that educating of the child through music which is the reason for including this subject in the course of study.

II. Musical Applications

Children enter the school with greatly varying musical experiences and abilities — some can sing sweetly and some can scarcely sing at all; some respond sensitively and easily to the rhythmic sway of the music while others are apparently unmoved; practically all, however, enjoy listening to music.

The first school experience with music should be *listening* — to the teacher, the phonograph, the piano, or some other sweet-toned instrument. Very soon, however, the class as a whole, led by the more musical children, will want to *sing* attractive songs or parts of songs which have been sung to them. This group singing will disclose to a considerable extent the individual singing ability of the various children and will indicate what help is needed. The involving of children in simple *bodily movements* will likewise quickly indicate their abilities.

While the material under each sub-heading is printed in the order of increasing difficulty, the needs of the children and the particular objects to be accomplished with each unit and in each day or period will determine what will be used and how much shall be done with it.

III. Calls and Motives

1. *Bee.* 2. *Dove.* 3. *Cat.* 4. *Mother.* 5. *Child.* 6. *Conductor.* 7. *Echo.* 8. *Chick-a-dee.* 9. *Fly.* 10. *Creative Calls.* 11. *What Did You See?* 12. *Be-caws.*

This, or similar material drawn from other units or created by the teacher or children may be used (a) as little songs sung for their own sake by the teacher and by the children, (b) as introductory material for longer appropriate songs, such as those printed below under IV; (c) for tone-plays or games used with all the children or with the uncertain singers who need special help. The latter children should sing frequently for only a short interval at a time and incidentally rather than in a special period when they are separated from the rest of the children for tonal drill.

The teacher should sing only as many calls as are needed to lead the children to offer similar ones. When clear and simple ones are given which apparently please the children, she may ask if other children have heard these calls and if they can repeat them. Eventually every child, even the shyest and least musical, should share in repeating and even in contributing some calls.

At first the teacher will accept without criticism anything any child gives. Later she will, by encouragement and asking for closer listening, make each child consciously strive to imitate the model exactly. The teacher will bear in mind that frequently the trouble with children in this individual singing is not the lack of musical ability but the lack of practice and self-confidence.

IV. Songs

A. FOR CHILDREN TO SING. 1. *In School Together.* 2. *What Did You See?* (given above as III-11). 3. *Be-caws* (III-12). 4. *Rabbits.* 5. *The Brown Duck.* 6. *Swinging.* 7. *The Fairy Piper.* 8. *September and School.*

As noted above under II, songs in the very early school days should be presented primarily as listening material. Whatever song is selected may be sung by the teacher two or three times without accompaniment until she feels certain that the children understand the text and enjoy hearing it sung. (The use of the accompaniment should be delayed as long as possible and it should always be subordinate to the singing.)

If some of the children spontaneously sing along with the teacher, it is to be welcomed, but no attempt should be made to have all the children sing the song until unconscious assimilation by them has proceeded for a day or two. A second or a third song may be presented in the same way before the teacher tries to get the entire class to sing the first song.

The number of songs sung by the class as a whole will depend upon the needs and powers of the group and the amount of time devoted to the unit. Doubtless some children will be able to sing some of the songs individually and this, of course, should be encouraged. But the initiative for this sort of singing should come from the children rather than from the teacher.

B. FOR TEACHER TO SING TO CHILDREN. 1. *Sweet and Low.* 2. *My Violin.* In addition to the songs just discussed which the teacher sings

with the idea that most of the children will also eventually sing them, there may well be in each unit one or two songs which are a little more difficult and which only a few or possibly none of the children will be able to sing. These the teacher may occasionally present, either with her own singing or with a phonograph, in much the same way that she would present instrumental music to be listened to for its own sake.

C. SUGGESTIONS FOR SINGERS. All the musical experiences discussed in this and other units are significant for the education of children, but probably singing contains the most important possibilities. Song, properly used, may influence the child greatly, because through it he makes himself a living musical instrument. The forming of the child into a sensitive and expressive instrument is a delicate task for the teacher. To accomplish this she must always be more concerned with the child than with the song.

She must guide the widely different talents of the children. To stress the vocal aspects of a point already made, when children enter the school, some of them sing freely; some are so shy that they do not sing at all; some think as little about singing as they do about talking or shouting; to others it is a strange and wonderful experience. The teacher should strive to unite all the children gradually into a singing group. In song, they can express certain aspects of their lives in a particularly beautiful manner. Singing thus becomes a kind of improved speech — as meaningful as talking. Both are a part of fine living. Both help to make life more zestful and harmonious.

In this first unit, the teacher will have made a good beginning if the children enjoy listening to her singing, or the playing of a record, and take pleasure in trying to sing lightly and gaily some parts of the calls and the songs already discussed.

V. Rhythmic Plays and Dramatizations

A. SINGING GAMES. 1. *London Bridge.* 2. *Did You Ever See a Lassie?* Among the games which the children will recall having played during the summer will probably be these two. The excellent rhythmic training which they involve will usually make it desirable to play these games

2

in the school, both for those who know them and for those who may never have had the opportunity of playing them. They may, of course, be replaced or supplemented by other singing games which the children recall, if the teacher considers them valuable for rhythmic training. Simple directions for playing the games are printed with each song.

B. SPECIAL INSTRUMENTAL MATERIAL. 1. *On Tiptoe:* Gretry. A considerable amount of instrumental material for rhythmic movements is presented in the various units and this may be drawn upon for use at any time when it fits into the program. *On Tiptoe* may well serve as a continuation of the little song *The Fairy Piper* given under IV-A. Walking, running, tiptoeing, are among the most natural rhythmic movements of the children and may be utilized from the first day of school.

Great differences will appear in children due to aptitude and presence or absence of self-consciousness. Both participation and gain in control should be a natural rather than a forced growth. Children will eventually find their level happily if they are allowed to participate in their own way.

VI. Listening Material; Creative Music

A. FOR QUIET LISTENING. 1. *Prelude.* 2. *Waltz.* 3. *The Fairy Piper Plays.* 4. *Whispering Leaves and Trees.* Gentle music softly played may be used to induce quiet and to envelop the children in an atmosphere of loveliness. The teacher should have available a number of these pieces which are presented without discussion and are a contribution to that silent delight in music which is a part of everyone. The first two numbers are excellent examples. The piano or phonograph may be used, or any light-tone instrument which the teacher can play. Or the teacher may hum a melody or a song.

The third and fourth selections are to be used to begin that more thoughtful observation which is needed to supplement the general emotional reaction. In endeavoring to find the answers to the simple questions printed in the introductory stories, the children will need to

listen to the music throughout and will thus be started on attentive listening.

B. FOR RHYTHMIC EXPRESSION. 1. *On Tiptoe:* Gretry. The instrumental material which is listed under V-B may well be played for listening only, before it is used for rhythmic expression. In fact, this may serve as the test of its desirability for rhythmic expression. If, when it is played for listening, there are not at least half of the children who say that they would like to do something with the music, it probably will be wise to use it only for listening until they do express a desire. The type of bodily expression should, at least at the beginning, be left entirely for the children to decide, either individually or by approval of the group.

Creative music should receive constant consideration. Suggestions are printed from time to time under the seven larger headings of each Unit. Encourage the children to make suggestions regarding various ways of singing, playing, and moving.

VII. Rhythm Band

A. The rhythm band should come about only with gradual development and after a very modest beginning. For instance, one child and eventually two, or as many as four may, with light rhythm sticks, indicate the walking of children, in *September and School*, by tapping with the sticks on the first and second beats of each measure; likewise the first beats in *London Bridge* or *Did You Ever See a Lassie?*

B. We may gradually build up, also, a repertory of little pieces which are to be used especially for this type of activity. *Join The Band* is presented in this unit. It may be used for two different kinds of instruments, such as rhythm sticks and triangles. It may be played once with one kind of instrument emphasizing the first beat throughout, using only the third and fourth and seventh and eighth measures. Another variation would be to have the sticks play during the first and second and fifth and sixth measures and the triangle during the third and fourth and seventh and eighth measures. It is essential always to subordinate the rhythmic instruments to the melody as played by the piano.

III. CALLS AND MOTIVES

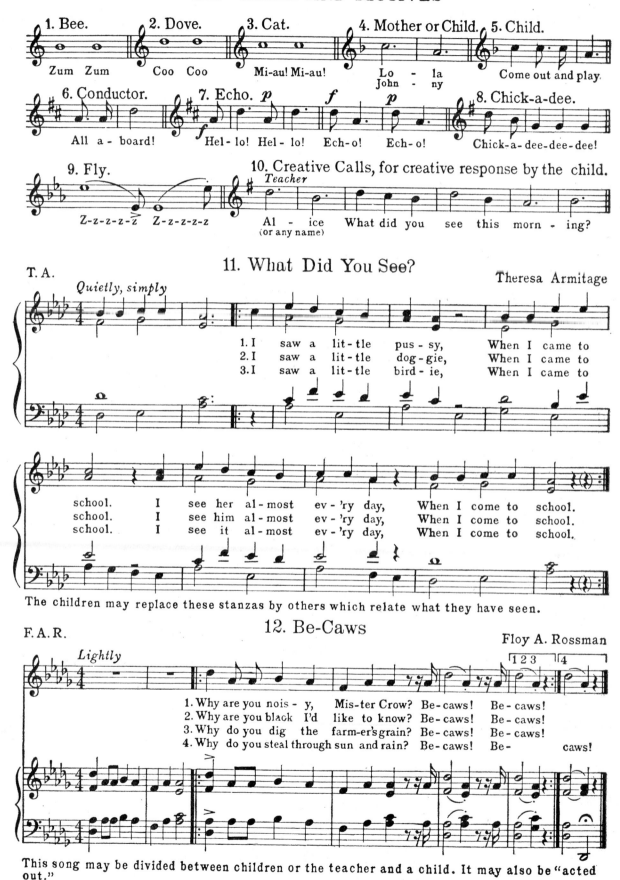

The children may replace these stanzas by others which relate what they have seen.

This song may be divided between children or the teacher and a child. It may also be "acted out."

4

IV. Songs

A. FOR CHILDREN TO SING

1. In School Together

1. Here we are in school, You're here, I'm here. Here we are in school, You and I.
2. Here they are in school, Ma-ry, Tom-my. Here they are in school, All are here.

2. What Did You See? (See III 11)
3. Be-caws (See III 12)
4. Rabbits

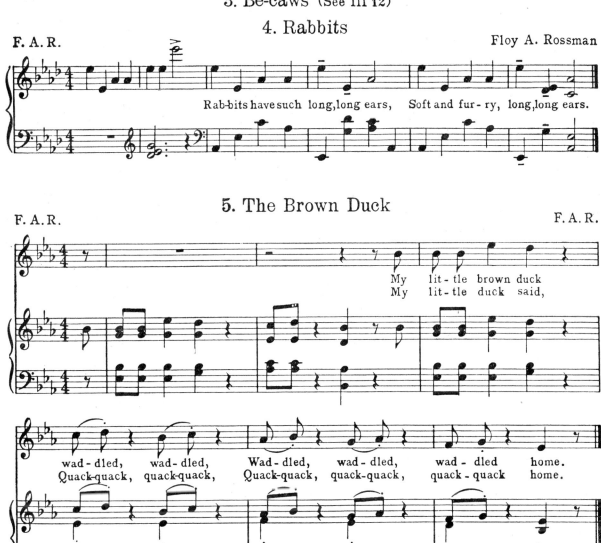

Floy A. Rossman

Rab-bits have such long, long ears, Soft and fur-ry, long, long ears.

5. The Brown Duck

My lit-tle brown duck
My lit-tle duck said,

wad-dled, wad-dled, Wad-dled, wad-dled, wad-dled home.
Quack-quack, quack-quack, Quack-quack, quack-quack, quack-quack home.

5

6. Swinging

1. Swing high, swing low, up we fly ____ Swing high, swing low, winds are rush-ing by. ____
2. Swing high, swing low, up we fly. ____ Swing high, swing low, soon we'll touch the sky. ____

One game of swinging may be played in groups of two. One child stands behind another, each balanced with the left foot foward. The first clings to an imaginary rope. The second rests both hands on the hips of the first, lightly pushing back and forth. The bodies sway as in a swing.

The second game is with groups of three. Two children face each other, clasping hands, making a swing board for an imaginary child. The third member stands between the two and lightly pushes the swing.

7. The Fairy Piper

1. The Fair-y Pip-er piped a song, Oo—
2. The breez-es bore it far a-long,

oo ____ oo ____

8. September and School

J.L.V.

Peter W. Dykema

Sep-tem-ber comes and the air is cool We are old e-nough and big e-nough to start in school.

B. FOR TEACHER TO SING TO CHILDREN
1. Sweet and Low

Alfred, Lord Tennyson

Joseph Barnby

Larghetto

Sweet and low, sweet and low, Wind of the west-ern sea. Low, low, breathe and blow, Wind of the west-ern sea. O-ver the roll-ing wa-ters go, Come from the dy-ing moon and blow, Blow him a-gain to me, While my lit-tle one, while my pret-ty one sleeps.

7

F.A.R.

Floy A. Rossman

I like to play my vi - o - lin, Hum _____

_____ I hold it close be - neath my chin, Hm _____

_____ Hm _____ Hm _____ I

hold it close be - neath my chin. Hm _____

V. RHYTHMIC PLAYS AND DRAMATIZATIONS

A. SINGING GAMES

1. London Bridge

Old Song

Directions: Two children join hands, raising them to form an arch or "bridge". The other children, in line, go under this arch, singing, circling around and going through again until the verse ends. On "Ladye", the children in the bridge drop their arms around the child who is passing under at that moment. They offer him a choice of two things, on which they have agreed before the game, such as "gold and silver". When the child has chosen, he stands behind the one in the arch to whom his choice belonged. Continue the game until each player has chosen. Then each child puts his arms around the child in front of him, the leaders join hands tightly, and the game ends in a tug of war.

2. Did You Ever See a Lassie?

Old Game Song

Directions: Single large circle, with a lassie (or laddie) in the center. Circle walks or skips to left. On "this way and that" circle halts, and child in center shows the action to be imitated. For rest of song all imitate leader in rhythm. Repeat with a new leader.

1. On Tiptoe

André Gretry
Arranged by F. A. R.

VI. LISTENING MATERIAL

A. FOR QUIET LISTENING

1. Prelude

Frederic Chopin

2. Waltz

Johannes Brahms

Children are walking in the deep woods. From far away they hear a sound that seems like a fairy playing on a little flute. By listening carefully to the music, can you tell just how many times the fairy piper played—once, twice, or three times? If desired, the children may, later, act the story, walking through the woods, stopping when the piper's tune is played.

3. The Fairy Piper Plays

Peter W. Dykema

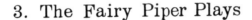

The following three-part composition may be used both for quiet listening and for rhythmic expression. The following lines recited or read by the teacher will serve to induce a spirit of attentive listening.

Tender green leaves are all whispering low,
No one can tell what they say.
Only the breeze may talk with the trees,
We hear them at close of the day.

Strong winds sweep the sky,
Great trees standing high.
Swing, sway, swing, sway,
Swing, sway.

The following hints may be utilized for rhythmic activity after the children have discussed the piece as pure listening material. The whispering of the leaves may be suggested by light rubbing of the hands together in time with the music of the first eight measures. During the final two measures of this section, the children may slowly lift their arms above their heads so that they may be in position for the swaying branches of the trees. The swaying should be slight at first, increasing and diminishing the movement as the music becomes louder and then softer. The whispering of the leaves should be resumed on the repetition of the first section while the hands are still high. The bodies continue the swaying of the trees as the hands are slowly lowered.

4. Whispering Leaves and Trees

Floy A. Rossman

B. FOR RHYTHMIC EXPRESSION (See On Tiptoe, V B)

VII. RHYTHM BAND
Join the Band

J. L. V.

UNIT TWO

The Home

I. *Guiding Educational Principles*

THE HOME IS THE center of the child's affections and activities. A unit of study based upon the home should not be restricted to a few school days, but should be often referred to during the year. Moreover, it is not necessary to complete the study of Unit One before introducing portions of Unit Two, nor is it desirable to assume that Unit Two adequately covers the subject.

Giving consideration in the school to the affairs of the home should not only help the child to feel more at ease in the school, should not only add variety and richness to the school program by drawing from the varied experiences of the children, but it should also aid the child to appreciate better how much he owes to the home.

II. *Musical Applications*

Music can add greatly in developing the affection and understanding with which the child regards his home. Many aspects of home life which seem natural and even commonplace due to constant repetition are seen in a different light and take on new interest when they are celebrated in song. The rhythmic presentation in games and dramatizations of some of the activities of the home introduces a fun element in what otherwise might be uninteresting routine. The emotional character of the music, sung or acted, or merely listened to, adds a glow of warmth and interest. The musical material presented in this unit suggests some of the possibilities which may be utilized by the teacher.

III. *Calls and Motives*
(Keys may be freely transposed)

1. *Clock.* 2. *Calling Mary.* 3. *Calling John.* 4. *I See You.* 5. *Play Call.* 6. *Hello!* 7. *Mother Calling.* 8. *Dinner Call.* 9. *Wait Call.* 10. *Telephone Call.* 11. *Cheerio* (with accompaniment). 12. *Game of Afternoon Tea.*

These calls, in text and melody, are closely related to the songs presented in IV and may be used both independently and in connection with them. They are thus to be considered as both pleasant tonal plays which, frequently repeated and imitated, are helpful in tuning the voices of the children and as little songs valuable for their own sake. The effect of these calls, as of the songs, is constructive in that each contains the suggestion of a helpful, considerate, and obedient child in the home. Vocally considered, these calls furnish additional material for brief participation in singing by each of the children. The game spirit must predominate.

IV *Songs*

A. FOR CHILDREN TO SING. 1. *When I Take a Walk.* 2. *My Dog Teddy.* 3. *Good Gingerbread.* 4. *Lullaby.* 5. *Visitors.* 6. *A Funny Pincushion.* 7. *Tick-Tock.* 8. *Pancakes.* 9. *Cookies.* 10. *A Good Idea.* 11. *My Bunny.* 12. *Useful.* 13. *Grace.* 14. *Baby's Prayer.* 15. *Sleep, Baby, Sleep.* 16. *A Drowsy Song.*

Just as the activities of the child in the home are of great variety, so the sixteen songs listed are of many kinds—vigorous and quiet, involving both what the child does and what he merely observes; serious and humorous, touching himself and his relations to others. Here are songs about helping in the home, receiving visi-

O-F-M—2

tors, eating, sleeping, the clock, playing with pets, saying prayers, going walking and other activities. Nearly all of these topics are included in other units, sometimes at greater length. The teacher will, as usual, feel free to use any material that fits the powers and needs of the children.

If, after the teacher has sung the song to the children, they are immediately interested in it, parts or all of it may be repeated until the children are able to sing it. Other songs which do not immediately interest the children may be discarded for the time being or may be presented some later day when it is possible the children may welcome them and thus make them subject for further study. Situations and children differ; but there is such a wealth of songs in this book that there should be no difficulty in finding material agreeable to all. Practically always, only those songs should be used which the children evidently desire to sing; thus most of the songs will be learned almost unconsciously because the children will so often ask the teacher to sing them.

B. FOR TEACHER TO SING TO CHILDREN. 1. *Two I Love*. 2. *A Prayer*. 3. *Swing, Cradle*. 4. *When Mother Sews*.

Four other songs dealing with home situations may be sung or played simply as listening material; but there is no objection to having these sung by some or all of the children provided they are learned without time being taken expressly to teach them. The teacher, however, may feel free to interchange material in IV-A and IV-B whenever it is wise. From time to time, also, the children may listen to any individual or small group from the class who can sing any of these songs effectively.

C. SUGGESTIONS FOR SINGERS. One of the best means of leading the child to think of song as vital expression is the use of musical conversations, the phrases or sentences at first consisting of only two different tones. The teacher, for instance, may sing to the children Call 1; to which the children, using the same tune, reply with Call 2.

Other phrases may be used, such as "Where is John?" with the reply, "I'm here." The teacher may suggest to the children that they use this phrase for greeting the folks at home, singing "Hello, Daddy!" or "Hello, Mother!"

On other days different sequences of tones may be used, with the same or similar texts, such as in Call 3.

(1) How are you? (2) Ver-y well. (3) How are you?

V. Rhythmic Plays and Dramatizations

A. SINGING GAMES. 1. *Here We Go Round the Mulberry Bush*. 2. *Looby Loo*. 3. *Knock at the Door* (a play for baby).

These traditional game-songs present, as good fun, activities of the home which are not always fun in reality. Possibly, the game spirit of the school may with profit be carried into the home.

These three games may be used in other units just as *Did You Ever See a Lassie?*, in Unit One, may be adapted for use in our study of the home. Several of the songs listed under IV-A can be used for dramatization and for rhythmic movement. Consider numbers 1, 2, 4, 5, 7, 8, 9, 12.

B. SPECIAL INSTRUMENTAL MATERIAL. See B under next heading.

Just as bodily movement is a sign of life, so rhythmic expression is a sign of control. No normal child has to be taught to make motor responses, but, with many children, ordered rhythmic movements must be developed. Until controlled rhythmic expression becomes natural, even automatic, all effort tends to be haphazard and wasteful of energy.

Each child, being somewhat different in structure from every other child, has a rhythm which is his own. This personal rhythm should be studied and respected by the teacher. When freedom of expression has been established, the movements of the child frequently reveal tendencies, powers and weaknesses which are so characteristic of physical and mental make-up that the observant teacher is greatly aided in understanding the needs of the child.

While it is possible to obtain rhythmic expression without music—as in many natural physical activities, such as running, galloping, swaying, hauling, pounding, sawing—the prevailing rhythmic swing of music is a pleasant and powerful incentive to rhythmic expression.

VI. *Listening Material*

A. FOR QUIET LISTENING. To supplement the vocal lullabies given under IV-A, we present two lovely examples of instrumental music. 1. *Cradle Song* by Schumann and 2. *Loss* by Gurlitt. This material is again to be presented with only a slight amount of discussion since its purpose is merely to surround the children with pleasant sounds and to allow them to enjoy it in their own way.

We include, however, two little pieces which may be used for observation and discussion by the children. In each of these there are two sharply contrasting portions one of which the children are to choose and indicate when they have recognized it. A little story is suggested for the first; the idea of a high and a low voice in conversation is sufficient to provide a focus for listening to the second. 3. *A What and When Puzzle* (*The Clock Store; Rossman*). 4. *A Conversation;* Haydn.

In all listening periods, whether they are while the children are sitting quietly or are developing some rhythmic expression, the teacher may well bear in mind the old saying, "Haste makes waste." Formalizing or hurrying the listening portion of the program, trying to develop predetermined answers, will almost inevitably work against the main purpose of these suggestions for listening, namely, developing in the child self-reliance and honest individual taste. The reason so few adults have worth while convictions about music is usually due to their having been "told the answers" when they were young.

B. FOR RHYTHMIC EXPRESSION. All of the compositions presented under VI-A lend themselves also to rhythmic expression of a gentler nature than that called for under V. Thus we may have swaying or rocking the cradle with the Schumann and Gurlitt numbers, the movement of the pendulum in *The Clock Store* and one or two persons entering into conversation in the final number.

VII. *Rhythm Band*

A. MATERIAL DRAWN FROM PRECEDING HEADINGS. The rhythm sticks and triangles used in Unit 1 will be sufficient for use in Unit 2. These may be introduced with material of III-1 or IV-A 1 (sticks) ; IV-A 4 (triangle) ; IV-A 15 (triangle in first four and last four measures only) ; VI-A 1 (triangle) ; 2 (triangle) ; 3 (sticks).

B. SPECIAL MATERIAL. 1. *Waltz: Southern roses*, Strauss.

This thirty-two measure section of a waltz is, as usual, made up of four passages of eight measures each. If the thirty-two measures seem too long for the children at this stage of their development, half of the material may be used by omitting the first ending and the repetition of the first eight measures. After the children have become well acquainted with this, they will probably enjoy using the remainder. It may be treated in several ways: (a) only the first pulse in the measure may be marked, either by rhythm sticks and triangles together, or by triangles alone in the first four measures and in the next to the last four measures (in both the first and second endings), with the sticks playing in all the other measures; (b) the triangle may play the first half of each strain (four measures), striking only on the first beats, and the sticks may play each of the three beats in the second half of each strain; (c) in addition to what is suggested under (b), the triangles may strike the first beat of each of the last four measures.

These suggestion are, of course, intended only for the guidance of the teacher in her discussions with the children. The editors, however, would like to emphasize the idea that in all creative activity the general feeling for the music as a whole is more important than any detail. In the rhythm band, for instance, the music as played by the piano, without special emphasis, and certainly without pounding, should always stand out above the rhythmic touches added by the children's instruments. The children should always feel that they are decorating or stressing portions of what the piano plays, rather than doing something which is significant in itself.

III. Calls and Motives

This is adaptable for a small group where chairs may be placed in a circle. One is chosen "hostess," who "passes the tea." The arrival and departure of guests may be included, with "How-do-you-do?" "I'm glad to see you." "Good-bye." etc.

16

IV. Songs

1. When I Take a Walk

Floy A. Rossman

F.A.R.

1. When I walk a - long the street,
2. When I walk a - long the street,

left, right, left, right, I smile at all the friends I meet, left, right, left, right.
left, right, left, right, I bow to all the friends I meet, left, right, left, right.

2. My Dog Teddy

F.A.R.   F.A.R.

1. He runs a - round all day. He's
2. He steals my Dad - dy's shoe, And

al - ways in the way. He barks and is a nui - sance, But he's my dog, Ted - dy.
Moth - er's slip - pers, too. But ev - 'ry - bod - y loves him, For he's my dog, Ted - dy.

17

3. Good Gingerbread

J.L.V.

J. Lilian Vandevere

1. Gin-ger-bread, gin-ger-bread, Moth-er likes to
2. Gin-ger-bread, gin-ger-bread, Moth-er stirs and

make it. Gin-ger-bread, gin-ger bread, Moth-er likes to bake it.
beats it. Gin-ger-bread, gin-ger-bread, I'm the one who eats it.

4. Lullaby

F.A.R.

F.A.R.

Bye - lo -

Pedal each measure

bye, go — to sleep. Go to

18

sleep. _____ Twink - ling stars watch _ will

keep, watch will keep. _____

5. Visitors·

1. When vis - i - tors come It's
2. When vis - i - tors go It's

fun to say, "Oh, how - do - you - do! Won't you come in?"
nice to say, "I'm glad that you came. Please come a - gain!"

6. A Funny Pincushion

Margery Armitage

Theresa Armitage

1. I have a lit - tle pus - sy cat, she sits out in the sun. She has the ver - y soft - est paws, a cush - ion on each one.
2. And they are real - ly cush - ions, for I know, with - out a doubt, One day when she was cross with me a lot of pins came out.

7. Tick-Tock

J. Lilian Vandevere

Harvey W. Loomis
Accomp. by Peter W. Dykema

Rather fast, with a light tinkling sound

My clock is just a ti - ny, thing, It's ver - y round and small, You
When I am sleep - ing cos - i - ly, In blank - ets warm and thick, My

8. Pancakes

J.L.V.

J.L.V.
Accomp. by P. W. D.

Briskly and lightly

1. Pan - cakes,   come and turn them, Pan - cakes,
2. Pan - cakes,   you can make them, Pan - cakes,

up - side down. Pan - cakes,   I pre - fer them nice and brown.
it is fun. Pan - cakes,   come and eat them, now they're done

9. Cookies

J.L.V.

J.L.V.

1. Stir, stir, mix and beat.
2. Cut, cut, round and neat.

Out in the kitch - en Moth - er's bak - ing. Roll, roll,
How man - y pans is Moth - er mak - ing? One, two,

roll them thin. Big gin - ger cook - ies fill the tin.
may - be three. That means e - nough for lunch and tea.

10. A Good Idea

Theresa Armitage

Peter W. Dykema

Go to bed ear - ly with -

22

out an- y fuss. Wake up good na-tured, and smile at us.

11. My Bunny

J.L.V.

J.L.V.
Accomp. by F.A.R.

There's noth-ing so soft as a bun-ny, ___ A

wee lit - tle, soft lit - tle bun - ny. ___ He will hop on his toes, he will

wig - gle his nose, And his pow - der - puff tail is quite fun - ny. ___

R.H.

12. Useful

13. Grace

14. Baby's Prayer

Old Rhyme

Harvey W. Loomis

I see the moon,—— the moon sees me.—— God bless the moon—— and God bless me.

15. Sleep, Baby, Sleep

Old Folk Song
Accomp. by P. W. D.

Sleep, ba - by, sleep, Thy fa - ther guards the sheep. Thy moth - er shakes the dream - land tree, And down fall pleas - ant dreams for thee. Sleep, ba - by, sleep. Sleep, ba - by, sleep.

25

16. A Drowsy Song

J.L.V.

Samuel Drake
Accomp. by Gladys Pitcher

All a - round me, all a - round me, All a - round me
Shad-ows found me, shad-ows found me, Shad-ows found me

shad-ows creep. fast a-sleep. A-sleep a - sleep, a - sleep, a - sleep

rit. > p > p > pp > pp

Ped. ❋ Ped. ❋ Ped. ❋ Ped. ❋

B. FOR TEACHER TO SING TO CHILDREN

1. Two I Love

J.L.V.

J. Lilian Vandevere

1 When school is out A -
2. When ev - 'ning comes, I

way I go, At home there's some - one wait - ing I know. She's
watch the street, Un - til I hear two hur - ry - ing feet. Then

wait - ing each day, And I   hug her and say,   Moth-er! Moth-er!   Moth-er!___
some - one comes by, And I   hug him and cry,   Dad - dy! Dad-dy!   Dad - dy!___

2. A Prayer

J.L.V.

H. W. L.

1. Heav'n-ly Fa - ther,   make us gen - tle,   Quick   to work and   kind   in play.
2. Guide and guard us,   make us lov - ing,   Keep   us hap - py   all   the day.

3. Swing, Cradle, Swing

Old Song
Accomp. by P. W. D.

With a gentle swing

1. Ba - by is   a   sail - or boy,   Swing, cra - dle,   swing.___
2. Nev - er fear, the watch is set,   Swing, cra - dle,   swing.___

Sail - ing is   the sail - or's joy,   Swing, cra - dle,   swing.___   Swing, cra - dle,   swing, cra - dle,
Storm-y gales are   nev - er met,   Swing, cra - dle,   swing.___

swing, cra - dle,   swing.___   Swing, cra - dle,   swing, cra - dle,   swing, cra - dle,   swing ___

4. When Mother Sews

Stephen Fay

Czechoslovakian Tune
Accomp. by Gladys Pitcher

When my moth - er sits and sews, In and out her nee - dle goes; Moth - er sews such love - ly things, And while she sews she hums and sings,___ Hm___

V. RHYTHMIC PLAYS AND DRAMATIZATIONS

A. SINGING GAMES

1. Here We Go Round the Mulberry Bush

Old Singing Game

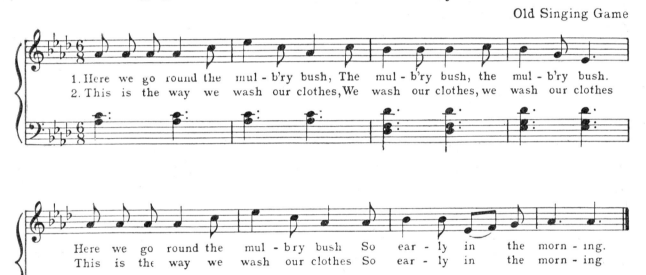

1. Here we go round the mul - b'ry bush, The mul - b'ry bush, the mul - b'ry bush.
2. This is the way we wash our clothes, We wash our clothes, we wash our clothes

Here we go round the mul - b'ry bush So ear - ly in the morn - ing.
This is the way we wash our clothes So ear - ly in the morn - ing

3. This is the way we iron our clothes, etc.

4. This is the way we mend our clothes, etc.

5. This is the way we sweep the floor, etc.

6. This is the way we bake the bread, etc

7. This is the way we scrub the floor, etc.

8. This is the way we go to church, etc

Directions: Players in circle, hands joined. Move in circle singing first verse. In the second and following verses the action indicated in the lines is given in pantomime. Usually after each new verse the first verse is repeated as a chorus.

2. Looby Loo

Old Singing Game

4. I put my right foot in, etc.

5. I put my left foot in, etc.

6. I put my head 'way in, etc.

7. I put my whole self in, etc.

This game may be presented as telling a story about a boy who took a hot bath every Saturday night. One night the fire went out and he had to bathe in cold water. Each player represents the boy. (A) All join hands in a circle and skip to left, repeating this after each verse of pantomime. (B) Pantomime, stand facing center, put right hand in toward center, gingerly; snatch it out, shake it vigorously and turn in place. Repeat as indicated by words of succeeding verses. On last verse all jump into center, out again, shake themselves, turn and finish with **a final stamp** or shout on "Oh".

3. Knock at the Door
A Play for the Baby

Knock at the door,   Peep in,   Lift the latch and walk   in.

Gestures: *Tap forehead,*   *lift eyelid,*   *Pull up end of nose, put finger in mouth.*

VI. LISTENING MATERIAL

A. FOR QUIET LISTENING

1. Cradle Song

Robert Schumann

2. LOSS

Cornelius Gurlitt

A lady was walking down the street one afternoon when she passed a store from which some odd sounds were coming. Can you tell what kind of store it was, and what time it was when she passed the store?

On various repetitions, the teacher should change the number of the hour strokes of the clock.

3. A What and When Puzzle
(The Clock Store)

Floy A. Rossman

4. A Conversation

Franz Joseph Haydn
String quartet N° 3

From *Rossman Piano Series*   Bk II- C. C. Birchard & Co.

VII. Rhythm Band

B. SPECIAL MATERIAL

1. Waltz: Southern Roses

Johann Strauss

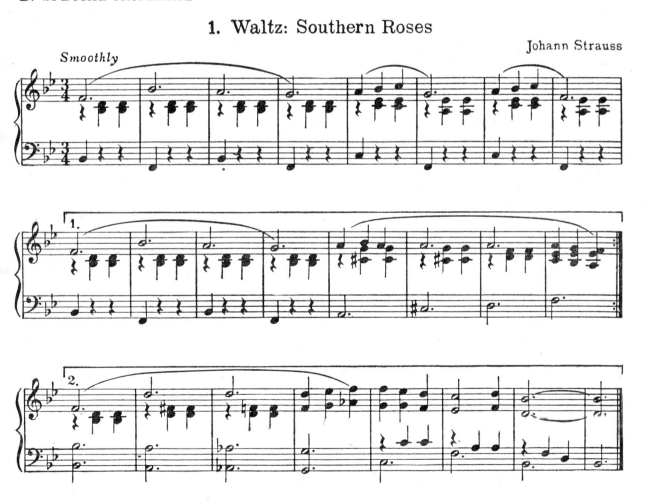

UNIT THREE

Autumn

I. Guiding Educational Principles

INCE THE CHILD IS always in the midst of one of the seasons, and since the seasons extend throughout the year, it is obvious that no one unit of study can include all needed material. As will be seen from consulting our headings, the seasons are divided into Autumn, Winter, Spring, and Special Days. Other topics which have strong seasonal interest are Thanksgiving, Christmas, the patriotic days of February, and finally, at the close of the year, Traveling.

As seasonal interests make themselves felt during the year, material may be drawn from not only the unit which is particularly appropriate at the time, but from any other unit which may be helpful. Interest in the changing year is natural for children, and, if properly guided, may become a delight through later life.

II. Musical Applications

As the child is naturally interested in the changing colors and moods of autumn, and the freer activity which the cooler weather brings, so he is naturally interested in music which deals with these topics. It will be noted that the musical material listed below is related not only to the changes in nature during the autumn months, but also to interests and activities which attract children at this season of the year. Suggestions for vigorous out-of-door sports and activities predominate. But there is also in the music an occasional touch of that quiet contemplation of the closing year, which even children sense to some degree.

III. Calls and Motives

1. *Shepherd's Call*, developed later into the song, *Coo-ee*, 1a. 2. *Owl calls*, developed into the song, *The Owl*, 2a. 3. *Echo calls*, developed into the song, *Echo*, 3a. 4. *Horn call*, developed into *Little Hunting Song* by *Schumann* (see VB).

The singing of the calls in the play spirit may precede by two or three days the presenting of the longer compositions. The children will be interested in recalling the little phrases which they have sung, and seeing how they have grown into longer pieces. This procedure is foundational for much, if not all, music study.

IV. Songs

A and B. FOR CHILDREN TO SING AND TO HEAR THE TEACHER SING. 1. *The Weather Vane*. 2. *The Bird's Lullaby*. 3. *It's Fall*. 4. *October*. 5. *Fall Colors*. 6. *Bobbing for Apples*.

These songs have a considerable variety of mood, ranging from vigorous play to quiet meditation. Some classes will not be interested in learning the quieter songs, although they will enjoy hearing the teacher sing them. But even if the children desire to learn them, there is no necessity of breaking the songs into parts for teaching purposes.

It seems probable that our children would develop into more capable adult musicians if throughout their school course they had been trained to sing entire songs, suitable, of course, in length and difficulty to their years. They would then need to focus upon the structure or individual tones of phrases or patterns only when these do not come out right in their attempts to reproduce entire songs. Short, simple songs such as most of these, which the children

34

will almost unconsciously learn after the teacher has sung them on two or three days, are excellent for demonstrating this method of teaching by whole rather than parts.

C. SUGGESTIONS FOR SINGERS. There is such a close relation between rhythmic expression and good singing that little rhythmic plays involving reciting or singing by the children should be introduced early. For instance, the teacher may recite to the children this rhyme:

"Humpty Dumpty sat on a wall,
Humpty Dumpty had a great fall."

The teacher speaks the two lines with a strong rhythmic accent. The children repeat the words in a light speaking voice, also with a strong accent.

Then the teacher may clap the rhythm and ask the children if they know what words fit what she has been clapping. Then all the children may tap the same rhythm lightly.

The children say the words in rhythm again, and raise and lower their hands over their heads, making an up and down movement in each measure. As they come to the final word, they may drop hands, voices, and the entire body on the word "fall." Then all of these movements may be repeated with the singing of the song as indicated by the music below:

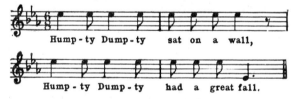

V. Rhythmic Plays and Dramatizations

A. SINGING GAMES. 1. *I'm Tall, I'm Small.* 2. *Hunting.*

These two old games, suitable for out-of-door playing as well as in the schoolroom, should be played very rhythmically, while still expressing a free, happy spirit.

B. SPECIAL INSTRUMENTAL MATERIAL. 1. *Little Hunting Song*, Schumann.

Since this rollicking number by Schumann is longer than any other composition we have thus far had for rhythmic expression, only a part of it may be used at first—such as the opening and the closing eight measures. It lends itself to dramatization (the gathering of the party summoned by the horn, in the first part, the riding to the hunt and the return home in the second part), and also to free rhythmic expression, with running or galloping or the imitation of riding on horses.

The following quotation from Dr. Helen Christianson states succinctly the significance of bodily rhythmic movements to young children:

The young child makes a functional use of music, as did the folk, finding in this medium a satisfying outlet of emotion or mood—joyousness, whimsicality, adventure, wonder. Again, his whole body becomes an instrument vibrating in response to gay rhythmic music. Such whole-hearted integration of thought, feeling, and movement has a significant bearing, both on the child's growing enjoyment of music, and on his social and emotional development.

VI. Listening Material

A. FOR QUIET LISTENING. 1. *Waltz*, Op. 12, No. 2, Grieg. 2. *Theme* from Sonata IX, Mozart. 3. *Chanson Triste*, Tchaikovski.

These numbers present moods of subdued merriment; light, happy grace; and quiet contemplation. If the Grieg and Tchaikovski selections are too long, portions only may be used at various times, such as the last eight measures of the Grieg and the last four or twelve measures of the Tchaikovski.

VII. Rhythm Band

A. MATERIAL DRAWN FROM PRECEDING HEADINGS.

If a sweet-toned bell or dinner gong can be obtained, it may now be added to the sticks and triangles used in the first two units. The bell or the triangle may be used in IV A 4, the triangle in IV A 5, and the triangle and the sticks in IV A 6. For most children the striking of only the first beat in the measure is still sufficient, but in the latter number some of the more capable children may emphasize the second and third beats with the rhythm sticks, and the triangle or bell may accent the first beat.

B. SPECIAL MATERIAL. 1. *Triangles and Bells*, Loomis. 2. *Musette*, Gluck.

Triangles and Bells may be treated in the same way as IV-A 6. However, in this number and the *Musette*, the teacher may allow the children to suggest their own instrumentation.

III. Calls and Motives

1. Shepherd's Call

Coo - ee, coo - ee, coo - ee.

2. Owl Calls: Big Owl

Hoo - hoo - hoo - hoo.— Hoo - hoo.—

Little Owls

Hoo - hoo - hoo-oo. Hoo - hoo - hoo hoo. Hoo-hoo-hoo-hoo-hoo-hoo-hoo-hoo-hoo.

3. Echo Calls

Hel - lo, hel - lo, Hel - lo, hel - lo, Hel - lo, hel - lo.

f *f* *p* *p* *f* *p*

4. Horn Call

Ta-ran-ta-ra-ta - ra.—

1a. Coo-ee

F. A. R.   F. A. R.

1. Shep-herds   call;   "Coo - ee,   Coo - ee,   Coo - ee."
2. Oh,   so   clear,   "Coo - ee,   Coo - ee,   Coo - ee."
3. Far   and   near,   "Coo - ee,   Coo - ee,   Coo - ee."

2a. The Owls

F. A. R.   Floy A. Rossman

The big owl calls from the old oak tree,

Hoo, hoo, hoo, hoo, hoo-oo! The three lit - tle owls blink their

3a. Echo Song

F. A. R.

Floy A. Rossman

eyes at me, Hoo-hoo-hoo-hoo-hoo-hoo-hoo-hoo-hoo-oo!

Hel-lo, hel-lo, hel-lo-lo. I

hear the ech-o ring-ing. I know the song I'm sing-ing will soon come back to

me. Hel-lo, Hel-lo, ech-o, hel-lo, hel-lo-lo.

IV. Songs

A and B. FOR CHILDREN TO SING AND TO HEAR THE TEACHER SING

1. The Weather Vane

F. A. R.

Floy A. Rossman

weath-er vane goes round and round Un-til a mer-ry wind Blows north, or

south, or east, or west. The weath-er vane goes round and round, And

nev-er stops to rest.

2. The Bird's Lullaby

A.B.

Alys Bentley

Peep, peep, peep says the lit-tle bird, Sleep, sleep, mur-murs the bush. Hush, hush, whis-pers the au-tumn breeze, Rest in your down-y nest. Peep, peep, hush.

3. It's Fall

J. Lilian Vandevere

Samuel Drake
Accomp. by J. L. V.

1. Yel - low leaves come down,
2. Birds that sang so long,

Float-ing one by one. Mead - ow land is brown, Sum-mer-time is done.
Far a - way they fly. Chirp-ing one last song, Tell-ing us good - bye.

4. October

J. L. V.

November

Peter W. Dykema

Quietly, but not too slowly

Here comes Oc - to - ber, Fields are turn-ing

No vember

days are getting

brown,___ On ev - 'ry breeze, from sleep - y trees, The leaves are drift - ing down.___

cold   The sky is gray The Winds do blow The rain comes pour

40

5. Fall Colors

J. L. V.

J. Lilian Vandevere

1. Gold-en-rod and as-ters, All your hands can hold.__ Sep-tem-ber wears a par-ty dress, Of lav-en-der and gold.__

2. Red for gay Oc-to-ber, See her danc-ing by.__ She likes to wear a crim-son gown, To match the sun-set sky.__

6. Bobbing for Apples

W. P.

William Peters

1. Ap-ple, ap-ple, ap-ple, ap-ple, Float-ing in a pan; ____ Bob-bing, bob-bing, bob-bing, bob-bing, Catch one if you can. ____

2. Ap-ple, ap-ple, ap-ple, ap-ple, Hang-ing on a string; ____ Bit-ing, bit-ing, bit-ing, bit-ing, Watch-ing ev-'ry swing. ____

V. RHYTHMIC PLAYS AND DRAMATIZATIONS

A. SINGING GAMES

1. I'm Tall, I'm Small

Old Game

Circle formation with one in center, eyes covered. A leader to indicate whether to be tall or small. 1. All stretch up tall. 2. All make themselves as small as possible. 3-4. Up and down again. 5. At signal from leader they take tall or small position and hold it. Center player guesses what the others are. If he is correct he chooses another to take his place.

2. Hunting

Old Game

The children may construct the game to suit themselves, one child being the fox, and the others the hunters. Occasionally there may be a dozen children who are capable enough to enjoy the game as outlined more formally in the following directions. Players in sets of about six couples stand in two lines, facing each other. Leading couple join hands, and slide eight steps down and back between the lines. Repeat. Second time: all face front. Head couple lead their lines around outside original lines. At the foot they make an arch under which the other pass, leaving head couple at foot. Repeat with new leaders. Players clap hands in time and sing throughout.

B. SPECIAL INSTRUMENTAL MATERIAL
1. Little Hunting Song

Robert Schumann, Op. 68, №7

VI. Listening Material

1. Waltz

Edvard Grieg, Op. 12, № 2

2. Theme

Wolfgang Amadeus Mozart
From Sonata in A Major

3. Chanson Triste

Peter I. Tchaikovski
Arranged

VII. RHYTHM BAND

B. SPECIAL MATERIAL

1. Triangles and Bells

Harvey Worthington Loomis

2. Musette

Sarah Olds

UNIT FOUR

Our Town

I. Guiding Educational Principles

 **W**HEN the child leaves the home to enter the school, he adds one important section to his enlarging world. In the town there are many other sections, with some of which he has already come into contact, and still others which he should gradually get to know. In the activities of the town lie great potentialities for the education of the child. If his contacts are happy ones, clarified by sympathy and understanding, he will be well started toward becoming a useful and helpful member of the larger society outside the home and the school.

Just as the school helps to interpret the home to the child, so it must help interpret other parts of the town. The little citizen of today and the big citizen of tomorrow will be greatly influenced by the interpretation which the school leads the child to make of the relations of himself to his environment.

II. Musical Applications

Song is a natural means of recording ideas and events which interest the child. The hearing and the singing of these songs and the acting of parts of them which lend themselves to dramatization will gradually familiarize the child with people and conceptions that he otherwise might not understand. Song, by presenting effectively certain aspects of the great world, helps give meaning and order to what otherwise might long continue to be a "big buzzing confusion."

In choosing musical material for "Our Town," therefore, the teacher should seek that which is both immediately attractive to the child and desirable for a better understanding of his environment. We present a large variety of songs in this unit and in other units containing related material. From these the teacher should select only that which is applicable to her own class and her educational plans.

III. Calls and Motives

1. *Train Whistle.* 2. *Factory Whistle.* 3. *Church Bell.* 4. *Auto Horn.* 5. *Newsboy.* 6. *Strawberries.* 7. *Pop-Corn!* 8. *The Scissors Grinder.* 9. *Grocery Store Calls.* 10. *Bell Peal* used in *Wagner's Parsifal.* 11. *Town Clock Chimes.* 12. "Good-bye," from *The Postman.* 13. "Hippity-hop," from *At the Grocery Store.* 14. "I like gum drops," from *The Candy Shop.*

We continue the practice, initiated in the preceding unit, of presenting motives or phrases from longer vocal and instrumental compositions with the hope that these will be both interesting in themselves and will serve as introductions to the complete compositions when the child meets them either in this unit or later.

From the numerous street sounds which are heard in many of the towns of our country we present fourteen which are comparatively common. Many of these will probably fit into any school program but some will have to be modified or replaced by others which are used in particular localities.

Since one object of the use of these calls is the developing of a pleasant singing tone, the teacher will not encourage the children to reproduce strident or raucous calls even though, frequently, the reproduction of them requires very keen tonal and rhythmic discrimination.

As was pointed out in Unit One, several types of creative activity may develop from the use of calls. Original dramatizing and the making of original songs are two natural results which frequently stimulate each other as the children consider the sights and sounds of the city or town. Singing the call of the taxi man, or dramatizing the movement of the taxi may develop into "our own song" about the taxi or the taxi man. The "whir" of the scissors grinder's wheel may inspire a song. The carnival ferris wheel or merry-go-round, or even the up and down of the elevator may grow into words and music.

One little child made up this song when a puppy appeared in the class room.

After the teacher had shown to the class a picture of fairies and elves several children offered snatches of song such as the following:

IV. Songs

A. FOR CHILDREN TO SING.

1. *My House.* 2. *I Like A Band.* 3. *The Postman.* 4. *The Bakery Shop.* 5. *At the Grocery Shop.* 6. *On the Bus.* 7. *At the Station.* 8. *The Milkman.* 9. *Tidy Town.* 10. *The Candy Shop.* 11. *Ice Cream Soda.* 12. *The Cobbler Shop.* 13. *The Barber Shop.* 14. *The Scissors Grinder.* 15. *The Organ Grinder.* 16. *The Church.*

From the songs printed in this unit the teacher will, from time to time, select those which fit into her program. The reception which the children give to a song when the teacher presents it should have an important bearing upon whether the song is to be retained for later periods, and is merely for the teacher to sing, or is for the children to learn so that they may sing it with or without her help.

B. FOR TEACHER TO SING TO CHILDREN.

1. *City Streets.* 2. *Taxi!* 3. *Song of the Milk Bottles.* 4. *Vesper Hymn.* 5. *How Lovely Are the Messengers.*

These additional songs will probably be too difficult for most of the children to sing. But any who wish to try may sing them along with the teacher after she has sung them several times for quiet listening. Moreover, both with these songs and those in the preceding group, the children may frequently be permitted to sing short portions of them, the teacher singing the remainder. Thus in *City Streets* they may sing only "I wonder"; in *Taxi!* only the first two words; in *The Song of the Milk Bottles,* the opening phrase "Rattle, Rattle, Rattle" whenever it appears; in *Vesper Hymn,* only "Amen" or, later, "Jubilate"; in *How Lovely,* the last phrase, "the gospel of peace."

C. SUGGESTIONS FOR SINGERS.

Children are naturally dramatic, that is, they project themselves into matters which engage their attention. When a child tells a story about a person or an animal, he speaks as though he were the person or animal. This dramatic tendency should be utilized in singing. Songs should be selected which permit the child to sing them easily as though they were expressions of himself. Encourage the singer to think of himself as expressing the ideas and moods of the song.

This feeling of dramatic impersonation will lead to vital "expression," so that each song takes on its own peculiar character. Songs which embody fine and appropriate emotions will cause the child to feel and express a certain measure of them, and will thus enrich his growing and developing self. The teacher should lead the child more and more to think of conveying to others the aspects of the song which he particularly enjoys.

V. Rhythmic Plays and Dramatizations

A. SINGING GAMES.

In connection with the songs under this heading, we have already given several suggestions for rhythmical activities. Some of those suggestions may be used with other songs if the children express such a desire.

In every town children play some of the traditional games already presented in preceding units. We add two others that are well known in some parts of the country. 1. *Hippity-Hop*; 2. *Sally Go Round the Chimney Pot*. These are given without accompaniments, as children would usually sing them.

B. SPECIAL INSTRUMENTAL MATERIAL.

Some of the rhythmical instrumental material presented in other units may be used in connection with Our Town. We add a jolly old English tune, *Poor Robin's Fancy*, which may be used as a skip, a march, or a simple dance.

C. CONTROLLED MOVEMENTS SUGGESTED BY A DRUM.

We may now add to our percussion instruments a small drum, or, better, a drum-head which is like a tambourine without the metal jingles. This instrument may be purchased at a low price or may easily be constructed. It has many uses when tapped lightly with the fingers or struck vigorously with the open or closed hand.

It may serve as an accompanying instrument in the rhythm band or, like a drum, as an independent instrument for guiding rhythmic bodily movements. Played slowly, it may lead the children in swaying,—slightly when played softly, and widely when played sharply. Playing the following patterns should indicate for the children various combinations of walking, running, and resting.

The above patterns may be introduced as independent material or they may be drawn from the melodies of various pieces of music which have presented to the children in this unit, such as VII-1 and 2; V-2; and VI-3. Suitable material will also be found in other units.

The teacher may well play these patterns on the drum at first, but eventually most of the children should be allowed to compose and play rhythmic patterns which a group of their mates will interpret with appropriate steps or movements.

VI. *Listening Material*

Outside the home and the school the child may hear music of Our Town in churches, in picture houses, in public concerts, in parks, on the streets in parades, and from wandering musicians. Since in each of these experiences a considerable variety of music may appear, there is a larger choice of appropriate material for quiet listening which the teacher may present. In this unit we give two examples: an old English tune based upon a church-bell peal, *The Bells of Osney*, and a tuneful melody from a duet in Verdi's opera *La Traviata*.

VII. *Rhythm Band*

The bell music which appears in this unit suggests the desirability of adding to our rhythm band instruments something with a deeper tone than that produced by the triangle. Bars of steel or the small crow-bars, sold in hardware or five-and-ten-cent stores, produce excellent bell-like tones when struck with a large nail. A graduated or tuned series of tones may be made by the children from various sizes of bottles into which the proper amounts of water have been poured.

Some of the children will be able to play with these bottles the 10th and 11th motives listed under III above (in the key of the bottles). For very bright children, the theme of *The Bells of Osney* is a possibility if six properly tuned bottles are available. With other compositions, such as the melody by Verdi, a single bar or bottle may be used as though it were a triangle.

For the rhythm band instruments which have been used in preceding units, several of the songs given under IV-A are suitable, especially 2, 5, 12, 13, 15.

III. CALLS AND MOTIVES

1. Train Whistle

Too - too-too - too

2. Factory Whistle

Whoo - oo - oo - oo

3. Church Bell

Ding - dong. Ding - dong.

4. Auto Horn

Honk!   Honk!   Honk-honk!

5. Newsboy

Morn-ing pa-pers!

6. Strawberries

Straw-ber-ries! All fresh!

7. Pop-Corn!

Pop - corn!   Pop - corn!   Hot   but-tered pop - corn!   Pop - corn!

8. "Ding-Dong" from The Scissors Grinder

Ding, dong, ding-a-dong, Ding, dong, ding-a-dong.

9. Grocery Store Calls

Ma - ry,   what did you buy?

Pe - ter,   what did you   see?

10. Bell Peal used in Wagner's Parsifal

Use "Ding-dong, Boom-boom," or other sounds.

11. Town Clock Chimes

12. "Good-bye" from The Postman

Good - bye,   good - bye,   good - bye.

13. "I like gum-drops" from The Candy Shop

I   like   gum - drops.

14. "Hippity Hop" from At The Grocery Store

Hip-pi-ty hop,   hip-pi-ty hop.

IV. SONGS

A. FOR CHILDREN TO SING

1. My House

Mary de Haven

Mary de Haven
Accomp. by F. A. R.

I know a house not far a-way, A house I live in

50

2. I Like a Band

Helen Fitch

Samuel Drake

1 The band starts to play, Far a - way down the street, And
2. The drum ma - jor leads, And he twirls his ba - ton. He

I hum the tune, keep-ing time with my feet I stand by the curb, And I
looks ver - y fine, as he comes march-ing on They play ver - y loud, And they

cheer when they come. I do like the sound of a big bass drum!
sound ver - y grand. I do like the noise of a - big brass band!

Rhythmic and dramatic activity: The children, divided into two groups, may alternate in being the band and the spectators, the one marching and imitating the playing of the various instruments, the other standing and singing.

3. The Postman

F. A. R.

Floy A. Rossman

Good morn-ing, Mis-ter Post-man, What did you bring?

POSTMAN A let - ter.
A pa - per.
A pack-age. (etc.)

CHILDREN Good bye! Good bye! Good bye!

4. The Bakery Shop

J. L. V.

J. Lilian Vandevere

1. The bak - 'ry shop has rolls and pies, Cakes of ev - 'ry kind and size. Cher - ry tarts, the yum - mi - est ones, And whole pans of cin - na - mon buns.

2. The bak - er makes the good white bread, Still, I choose whole wheat, in-stead. You should see the muf - fins - he makes, And oh, my, the choc - o - late cakes!

5. At the Grocery Shop

J. L.

Jane **Landon**

1. Hip-pi-ty hop to the gro-c'ry shop, For co-coa beans and
2. Hip-pi-ty hop to the gro-c'ry shop, An er-rand can be

tea; — For crack-ers and rice, For sal-mon and spice, And can-dy, just for me. —
fun. — I'm buy-ing some peas, Mo-las-ses and cheese, And shop-ping now is done. —

Rhythmic activity:—Skipping, singly or in pairs.

6. On the Bus

J. L. V.

J. L. V.

1. Here's the bus!
2. Through the town,

Here's the bus! Right on the cor-ner it stops for us.
Through the town, Watch for your cor-ner and then climb down.

7. At the Station

W. P.

William Peters

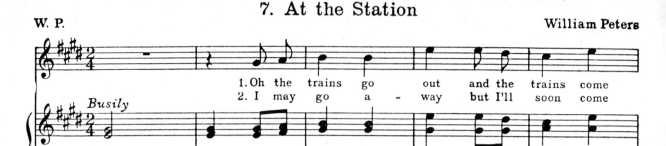

1. Oh the trains go out and the trains come back, But the rail-road sta-tion stands be-side the shin-ing track.
2. I may go a-way but I'll soon come back, To my lit-tle rail-road sta-tion by the rail-road track.

To leave his own town, or to welcome visitors to it, the child often goes to the railroad station. The text, with its rhythm of coming and going, leaves the station as the center of this activity.

Rhythmic dramatization:— One group of children may sing the song. Another may form lines, hands on the shoulders of the child ahead, and chug-chug about the room in time to the accompaniment. A third group may wave "good-bye" and "hello!" as the passengers depart or arrive.

8. The Milkman

J. L. V.

J. Lilian Vandevere

With the steady "clop, clop" of the milkman's horse

1. Through sun and rain, through win-ter and sleet, The milk-man is jog-ging a-long our street.
2. While we're a-sleep, his bot-tles clink - clink, He's bring-ing fresh milk for us all to drink.

9. Tidy Town

J.L.V.

J. Lilian Vandevere

1. The boy who likes to see things neat Will
2. The girl who likes a ti-dy town Will

nev-er throw pa-per A-round in the street.
nev-er tear pa-per, And then throw it down.

10. Candy Shop

F.A.R.

Floy A. Rossman

I like gum-drops, ev-'ry kind of lol-ly-pop,

Buy them 'round the cor-ner at the can-dy shop.

11. Ice Cream Soda

F. A. R.

Floy A. Rossman

What do we eat from a big tall glass? It's white and it's brown and it fiz-zes fast. It's a choc-o-late ice-cream so-da!

12. The Cobbler Shop

J. L. V.

J. L. V.

1. Hel - lo, Mis-ter Cob-bler,
2. Of course, Mis-ter Cob-bler,

Can you mend a shoe? The heel is ver - y
You can mend a shoe. The heel is straight as

Rhythmic activity:— The children may cross their legs and tap on a shoe sole in time to the rhythm of the introduction. The song may be dramatized with one or more cobblers and customers.

13. The Barber Shop

J. L. V.   J. L V

1. Snip, snip, snip, go the bar-ber's bus- y shears, A-
2. Dad- dy grins, and he gives a friend- ly wave, He's

cross my neck and be- hind my ears,   Snip, snip, snip,   as the
lath- ered white, for he wants a shave   Soon we're done,   and to-

bar- ber cuts my hair, While   I'm sit- ting high   in the   bar- ber chair
geth- er off we hop We're   both neat and trim from the   bar- ber shop.

14. The Scissors Grinder

F.A.R.   F.A.R.

Down the street comes the scis-sors grind-er,

Gay bells ring for the scis-sors grind-er, Ding, dong, ding-a-dong,

Ding, dong, ding-a-dong, Ding, dong, ding-a-dong, Ding, ding, dong.

15. The Organ Grinder

F.A.R.   F.A.R.

Moderato

Mechanically crisp

1. The   or-gan grind-er's   lit-tle tune goes
2. The   mon-key has a   coat of   red, and

round and round all day. We fol - low him a -
lit - tle cap of blue He holds it in his

bout and dance, Oh we like the lit - tle or - gan as it grinds a - way.
tin - y paws, Oh we like the lit - tle mon-key and the or - gan, too

16. The Church

W.P

William Peters

Ding dong! Ding dong! We hear the church bell

say It calls us to wor-ship, to sing and pray.

May be repeated softly

B. FOR TEACHER TO SING TO CHILDREN

1. City Streets

F. A. R.

Floy A. Rossman

Oh I like a sun-ny morn-ing on a cit-y street, With the beat, beat, beat of the man-y feet, And I like the hur-ry, hur-ry as the peo-ple go. And why they hur-ry so, I won-der!

2. Taxi!

J. L. V.

J. Lilian Vandevere

Tax-i! Tax-i! Roll-ing to and
Tax-i! Tax-i! All at once I'm

fro, I would like to ride, and I'll tell you where to go.
there. I have had the ride, and now I can pay the fare.

3. Song of the Milk Bottles

F. A. R.

Floy A. Rossman

Rat-tle, rat-tle, rat-tle, Hear the mer-ry warn - ing, That's the bus-y milk - man

Ear-ly in the morn - ing Rat-tle, rat-tle, rat-tle, Hear the bot-tles clink - ing,

Milk so fresh and sweet, For chil-dren to be drink - ing" Rat-tle, rat-tle, rat-tle,

Rat-tle, rat-tle, rat-tle Rat-tle, rat-tle, rat-tle

4. Vesper Hymn

Thomas Moore

Russian Air

Hark! the ves-per hymn is steal-ing O'er the wa-ters soft and clear;
Near-er yet and near-er peal-ing, Soft it breaks up-on the ear.

Ju-bi-la-te! Ju-bi-la-te! Ju-bi-la-te! A-men.

5. How Lovely are the Messengers

Isaiah

Felix Mendelssohn

Andante con moto

How love-ly are the mes-sen-gers that

preach us the gos-pel of peace, How love-ly are the mes-sen-gers that

sempre legato

preach us the gos-pel of peace, the gos-pel of peace.

V. Rhythmic Plays and Dramatizations

A. SONGS

1. Hip-pi-ty-hop

Popular American Game

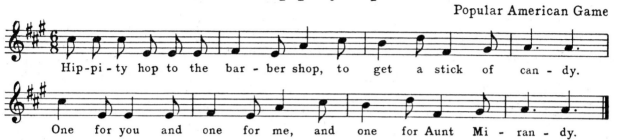

Hip-pi-ty hop to the bar-ber shop, to get a stick of can-dy.

One for you and one for me, and one for Aunt Mi-ran-dy.

For skipping, one child alone, or two or three with locked arms, or arms around each others waists.

2. Sally Go Round the Chimney Pot

American

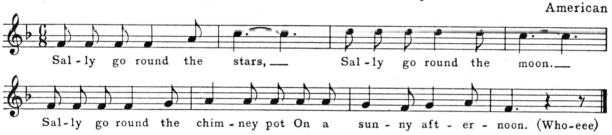

Sal-ly go round the stars, — Sal-ly go round the moon. —

Sal-ly go round the chim-ney pot On a sun-ny aft-er-noon. (Who-eee)

Directions. All join hands and skip in a circle to the right. At the end of verse shout "who-ee!" Kick forward with right foot and then circle left. Kick with left foot and circle right. Repeat as often as desired

B. SPECIAL INSTRUMENTAL MATERIAL

Poor Robin's Fancy

Dancing Master 1840
Arranged by F. A. R.

VI. Listening Material

1. Bells of Osney

virginal MSS. 1639

Osney Abbey is near Oxford. It is famous for the musical tones of its six bells, named Douce, Clement, Gabriel, Austin, Hantecter, and John.

2. Melody

(Dear Paris)

From La Traviata
Giuseppe Verdi

UNIT FIVE

Health and Safety

I. Guiding Educational Principles

THE health and safety movement which now has an important place in the school's educational program is based fundamentally on two ideas: (a) consciousness of how health and safety are promoted and (b) willingness, even enthusiasm, toward using these means. The responsibility for promoting these two ideas cannot effectively be assigned to a single subject or to a single period in the school day. Every opportunity must be seized for developing right habits of thinking and doing.

Music should not be called upon primarily to present new ideas concerning health and safety, but by making them more attractive it can do much to reinforce ideas presented in other subjects. Music has frequently made goodness a happy experience and it is increasingly being used to make health and safety precepts enjoyable as well as beneficial.

II. Musical Applications

Song can present health and safety precepts in clever and easily-remembered texts which are united with attractive melodies. Rhythmic games and actions carried on by groups of children cause correct posture and bodily carriage, deep breathing, and other good habits to be enjoyable instead of tiresome, as they frequently are when exercised by a single individual. Even listening lessons can, without sacrificing their musical content, contribute to the controlled relaxation necessary for health.

While this unit brings together a certain amount of special material for the health and safety program, the teacher will find in other units additional material which may be used for the same purpose. She will, of course, feel free to use all of the material at any time during the year when it is needed.

III. Calls and Motives

Short phrases or motives from songs may frequently be used as self-sufficient little calls. Examples in this unit are "Orange Juice" from *Good for You;* "Not I" from *Who Cares for the Rain?;* and "Sue (or any other name) can skip" from *A Skipping Song.*

Other motives, excellent for tuning the voices and sharpening the hearing, may be drawn from the multiple-toned horns with which many automobiles are now equipped. We present later several of these calls (involving not more than four different tones). These may be supplemented or replaced by others which are current in the local community.

IV. Songs

A and B. FOR THE CHILDREN TO SING AND TO HEAR THE TEACHER SING.

1. *Good For You.* 2. *Outdoors.* 3. *Fresh Air.* 4. *Would You?* 5. *Safety Lights.* 6. *A Friend in Need.* 7. *I Like These.* 8. *Do Take Care!* 9. *Rest.* 10. *Milk!* 11. *The Friendly Cop.* 12. *Who Cares for the Rain?*

In this unit we list no special songs which are primarily for the teacher to sing (except when the last four printed above prove to be too difficult for the children to sing easily). She should, nevertheless, feel free to use, for her singing only, any of those given. Moreover, the responsive singing of songs in which the teacher and children alternate in singing phrases is always enjoyable and helpful.

The more children get the idea that it is a privilege rather than a duty to join in the singing, the more spontaneous and effective will be the choral product. This procedure is especially helpful in encouraging the children who are shy or unaccustomed to singing. An attempt to join in group singing is the best introduction to that individual help which the teacher must frequently give to children who do not sing readily and in tune.

The songs selected for this unit are divided between the topics of health and safety.

C. SUGGESTIONS FOR SINGERS.

The acquiring of proper singing habits is greatly accelerated by the hearing of good models. The teacher should often sing to the children with light, pure tone. She may use both short songs and tonal patterns. As has already been exemplified, the latter may be either independent little pieces or motives drawn from songs or instrumental compositions which are later to be presented to the children. All of this singing by the teacher and the imitation of it by the children is simpler and is probably more effective if sung unaccompanied. But when necessary the piano may be used.

To avoid embarrassing those who are shy or who have not yet learned to sing alone, the singing by the children should, at first, be by the entire group, only those few children who are capable and desirous of singing alone forming occasional exceptions. After the group as a whole has sung enough to make this activity a natural and spontaneous procedure, individual singing should be gradually extended to all the children.

It is well to permit freedom in individual expression. Greetings such as "Good morning," "Good afternoon," "Good-bye," "Thank you," "How do you do?", may be either spoken or sung by teacher and child as the spirit moves. Some children will soon take pleasure in telling their own stories in song so that the idea suggested in the song, *What I Saw*, in Unit One, will gradually be considerably expanded.

V. Rhythmic Plays and Dramatizations

1. *We'll Follow.* 2. *We'll Dance.* 3. *A Skipping Song.* 4. *Bounce the Ball.* 5. *Play Ball.* 6. *Ring for the King!*

Rhythmic plays and vigorous games should, of course, make for good health and may assist also in developing habits of health and safety. These results are very largely dependent on the guidance of teachers who, while always stimulating responsibility and initiative in the children, should also see that moderation and consideration for others are observed.

In preceding and succeeding units, especially Unit Seven, will be found abundant material to supplement the above list.

VI. Listening Material

1. *My Cuckoo Clock*, Rossman. 2. *Music Box*, Musette, Gluck. 3. *Once There Was A Little Princess*, Kullak.

Since relaxation and composure are essential elements in health and safety, we present the above listening material which is to be used in quiet periods following vigorous activity.

VII. Rhythm Band

1. *Andante*, from Sonatine, Op. 36, No. 4, by Clementi.

A few of the more vigorously rhythmical songs, such as those in section V above, may be used for rhythm band playing, the children being allowed to indicate at what points in the music their instruments are to play. With these it is still sufficient if they play only on the first beat of each measure.

But with the quiet *Andante* by Clementi we may make use of two ideas, (a) having the children play on both the first and the second beats of each measure and (b) assigning the rhythm sticks, the drum, and the bars or bottles to one group for playing and the triangle to a place by itself. Thus in measures 5, 6, 7, 8, 13, and 14 the triangle may play alone while in the other measures all the rest of the instruments play. At the end the triangle may join with the others in playing once for each of the final six notes of the melody.

III. Calls and Motives

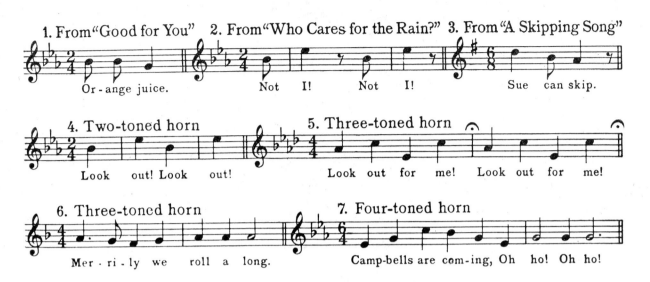

1. From "Good for You"   2. From "Who Cares for the Rain?"   3. From "A Skipping Song"

Or-ange juice.   Not I! Not I!   Sue can skip.

4. Two-toned horn   5. Three-toned horn

Look out! Look out!   Look out for me! Look out for me!

6. Three-toned horn   7. Four-toned horn

Mer-ri-ly we roll a long.   Camp-bells are com-ing, Oh ho! Oh ho!

IV. Songs

A and B. FOR CHILDREN TO SING AND TO HEAR THE TEACHER SING

1. Good for You

F. A. R   Floy Adele Rossman

1. A big glass of or-ange juice, or-ange juice,
2. A big ap-ple, ros-y red, ros-y red,

or-ange juice, A big glass of or-ange juice will start the day for you.
ros-y red, A big ap-ple, ros-y red, will make a lunch for you.

67

2. Outdoors

T. A.

Sarah Olds

Out - door games, in sun or snow, Keep you well and make you grow.

3. Fresh Air

J. L. V.

J. Lilian Vandevere

John o - pens his win - dow ev - 'ry night, So his cheeks are ros - y his eyes are bright.

4. Would You?

T. A.

Peter W. Dykema

Don't ev - er for - get to keep your shoes dry, But if they get wet, don't cry don't cry.

5. Safety Lights

F. A. R.

Floy Adele Rossman

Allegro

The red light is shin-ing, Don't cross the street! The green light is shin-ing, Look right, and left, Then go!

6. A Friend in Need

F.A.R.

Flóy Adele Rossman

Allegro

1. Oh, I have a friend, the doc - tor, a good friend, the doc - tor. He cares for me when I am ill. Oh, I have a friend, the doc - tor.
2. Oh, I have a friend, the den - tist, a good friend, the den - tist. He helps me when I ache with pain. Oh, I have a friend, the den - tist.
3. Oh, I have a friend, the school nurse, a good friend, the school nurse. She brings first aid with lov - ing care. Oh, I have a friend, the school nurse.

7. I Like These

J.L.V.

Sarah Olds

With decision

Beans, car - rots, fresh green peas, I like veg - a - ta - bles, I like these. Squash, spin - ach,

70

cab - bage, too, I like veg - a - ta - bles, yes I do!

8. Do Take Care!

J. L. V.

Peter W. Dykema

In walking tempo

Don't cross the street in the mid-dle of the square. Do take care, do take care! Don't cross the street in the mid-dle of the square, But wait till you come to the cor-ner.

9. Rest

J. L. V.

J. Lilian Vandevere

Aft-er you work, and aft-er you play, Then do you know what is best?— Curl up a while in an eas-y chair, and rest,— and rest.—

10. Milk

J. L. V.

Peter W. Dykema

A little sadly

Ted-dy was thin, and why, do you think?

Moderato

A little sadly

mf

mf Brightly

Ted-dy would nev-er take milk to drink. Bob-by was strong, and

mf

11. The Friendly Cop

J. L. V.

J. Lilian Vandevere

1. I like the friend-ly cop. When he holds up his hand, I
2. He keeps me safe, I know When he gives me a sign, I

stop._____ He's big and strong, he's ver-y kind, And so I watch, and
go._____ He guards us all, and so I stand Un-til he turns and

try to mind. I like the friend-ly cop. When he holds up his hand, I stop.__
waves his hand. He keeps me safe, I know. When he gives me a sign, I go.__

12. Who Cares for the Rain?

F.A.R.

Floy Adele Rossman

With my slick-er and my cap and my tall rub-ber boots, Who cares for the rain? Not I! It may driz-zle, it may pour, It may thun-der, it may roar! Who cares for the rain? Not I! Not I! Not I! Not I!

V. Rhythmic Plays and Dramatizations

1. We'll Follow

Folk Tune

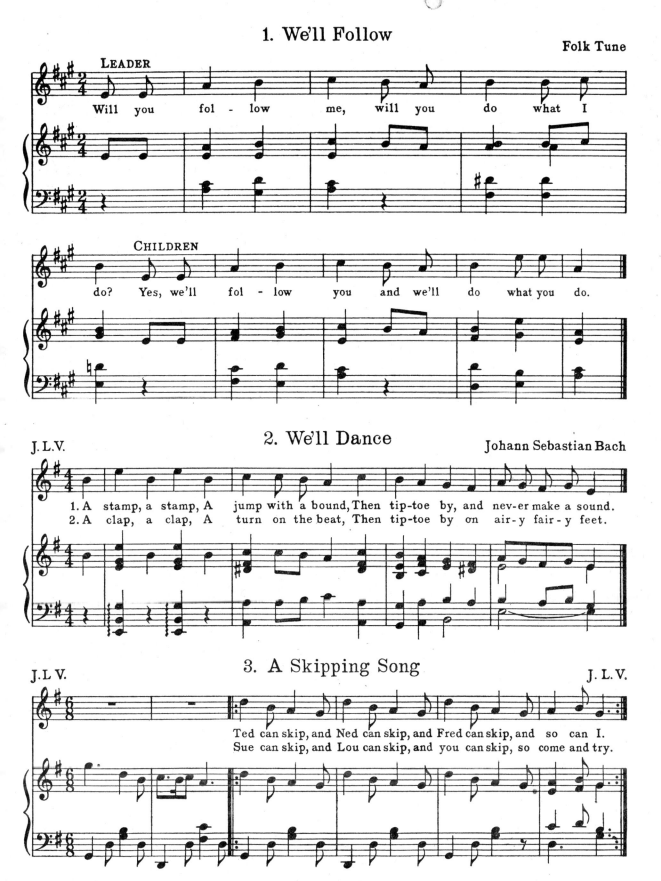

LEADER
Will you fol - low me, will you do what I

CHILDREN
do? Yes, we'll fol - low you and we'll do what you do.

2. We'll Dance

Johann Sebastian Bach

J. L. V.

1. A stamp, a stamp, A jump with a bound, Then tip-toe by, and nev-er make a sound.
2. A clap, a clap, A turn on the beat, Then tip-toe by on air-y fair-y feet.

3. A Skipping Song

J. L. V.   J. L. V.

Ted can skip, and Ned can skip, and Fred can skip, and so can I.
Sue can skip, and Lou can skip, and you can skip, so come and try.

4. Bounce the Ball

F.A.R.

Floy Adele Rossman.

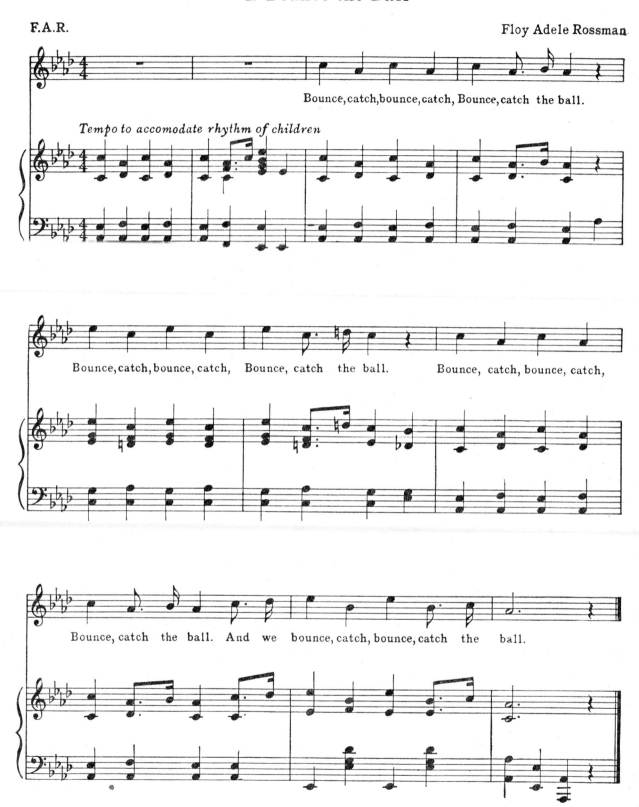

Tempo to accomodate rhythm of children

Bounce, catch, bounce, catch, Bounce, catch the ball.

Bounce, catch, bounce, catch, Bounce, catch the ball. Bounce, catch, bounce, catch,

Bounce, catch the ball. And we bounce, catch, bounce, catch the ball.

Let the children who are not bouncing the balls do the singing. If all have balls, it is advisable to use the words as a soft chant.

5. Play Ball

Margery Armitage

Maurice Jacquet

Bounce and catch my pret-ty red ball. I must be care-ful and not let it fall. Bounce and catch, If I let it drop, It's your turn to play, and I'll have to stop.

Simple crowns and a scepter instantly transform any small boy and girl into a King and a Queen. Singers and musicians may make up the lay members of the court. A Herald announces "Make way for the King! Make way for the Queen!" The trumpeters, with trumpet hands held high, announce the royal arrival.

Attendants to the King and Ladies-in-Waiting to the Queen add further dignity to the great procession. Impromptu thrones and attendants grouped about the King and Queen will complete the setting for the entrance of the royal personages or any other celebrities, imaginary or real, whom the children wish to honor.

6. Ring for the King!

F.A.R.

Floy Adele Rossman

Ring for the King, Ring for the King, Ring, ring the mer-ry bells, Oh,
Ring for the Queen, Ring for the Queen, Ring, ring the mer-ry bells, Oh,

ring for the King.
ring for the Queen.

Fine

Repeat softly D.S.

VI. LISTENING MATERIAL
1. My Cuckoo Clock

F. A. R.

I have a little clock hanging on my bedroom wall. A cuckoo lives in the wee house in the top of the clock. When the tiny door opens, my cuckoo comes out, flutters his wings, and sings:

Cuck-oo! Cuck-oo!

Sometimes I take a nap. What time is it when I go to sleep?

Cuck-oo! Cuck-oo! Cuck-oo!

What time does he waken me?

Cuck-oo! Cuck-oo! Cuck-oo! Cuck-oo!

I like to sing to myself as I go to sleep. What time does my cuckoo waken me, in the morning?

Note: A frequent change in the "time of day" will maintain the spice of concentration.

2. The Music Box

Musette, Gluck
Arranged by F. A. R.

79

Following the suggestion of Kullak's title, a program or story may be built up by the teacher or the children for this composition. The first part, Ⓐ (eight measures) and the last part, Ⓒ may well, with the horn calls, suggest a hunting party which approaches and then passes the castle in which the little princess lives. In the middle part, Ⓑ, the music with its light running figure may suggest that she hastens first to one part of the wall and then to another in order that she may obtain a glimpse of the passing riders on their horses. After the children have listened quietly to the music, they may wish to dramatize it according to the story which pleases them.

3. Once There Was a Little Princess

Theodore Kullak
Op.62, №1

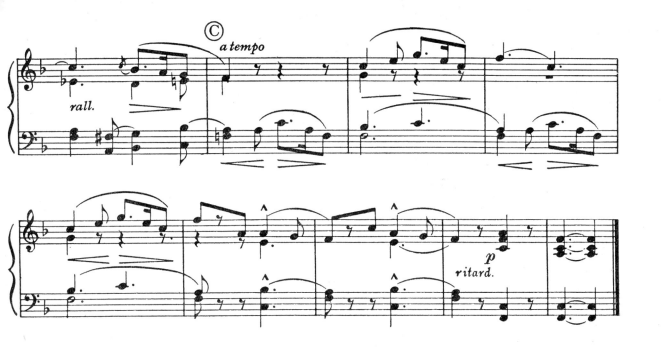

VII. Rhythm Band

1. Andante

Clementi
Sonatina, Op. 36, № 4

UNIT SIX

Special Days and Celebrations

I. Guiding Educational Principles

AN important concern of education and guidance is the wise and effective using of those moments in the life of a child when he is deeply moved. With a group of children these high spots appear frequently — daily, in fact — due to various individual causes. They are often of little interest to other children. But when the cause is of sufficient importance to interest all the children, a special period or special day may evolve for the group.

In addition to the important holidays of Thanksgiving and Christmas, for which special provisions are made with individual units, there are a number of other less widely celebrated occasions which may easily develop into red-letter days for the children as a group. These form the subject of the present unit.

The natural tendencies of the children to imitate, to repeat, and to enter heartily into any unusual activity will quickly unify the group in making these special days memorable ones. Properly used, they have great educational significance because of the willingness of the children to co-operate.

II. Musical Applications

Music, like all the other arts, helps both in celebrating any unusual event and enshrining it in an attractive form which can be used later for happy recalling of the event which it celebrated. In fact, we may almost use as a keynote in music instruction the idea that music makes happier both the present moment and the recalling of it. We present, therefore, a variety of material which at the proper times may be used very effectively.

The remark to be found in the preceding unit, concerning the use of the material, applies, of course, to the present unit.

III. Calls and Motives

1. *A Birthday Wish.* 2. *Happy New Year.* 3. *Valentine Questions.* 4. *Battle Hymn of the Republic.* 5. *Hail, Columbia!* 6. *The Strife is O'er.* 7. *The Flora Dance.* 8. *To the Colors.* 9. *Assembly.* 10. *Reveille.* 11. *Taps.*

Just as a cake with glowing candles is appropriate for every birthday, so music for one celebration may be used for similar celebrations. Such special music, like the birthday cake, is used to give a suitable tone to the occasion.

The items presented under this heading may be used for a variety of purposes; as introductory phrases which will acquaint the children with significant parts of songs which they will later sing; as helps and drills for the uncertain singers; as instrumental numbers which, played on the piano or trumpet, may stand by themselves as parts of a program or as illustrations in the regular music lessons; as motives which some of the children may pick out on the piano (all of the Army calls may be played on the black keys alone); and finally, as parts of songs which the children may sing as antiphonal responses when the teacher sings the other parts of the songs.

As usual, the teacher will select only such of the calls as are suitable for the needs and powers of the children. Small fragments of the Army calls are frequently more useful than the complete calls. They may be pitched in any key desired. Material from other units may supplement the motives in this one, and the Army calls will frequently fit in with other units.

IV. Songs

A. FOR CHILDREN TO SING. 1. *A Birthday Wish.* 2. *The Birthday Party.* 3. *Happy New*

Year! 4. *Our Flag.* 5. *For the Flag,* 6. *About Abraham Lincoln.* 7. *Valentine Questions.* 8. *We Sing of Washington.* 9. *The American Way.* 10. *St. Patrick's Day.* 11. *Easter Eggs.* 12. *A Tune About Trees.* 13. *The First of May.* 14. *For Mother's Day.* 15. *For Father's Day.*

With the exception of the songs for birthdays, which, of course, may come at any time of the year, the songs are arranged in chronological order, if we consider the flag songs related as much to the celebrations of Lincoln and Washington as to the Flag Day celebration on June fourteenth.

Since many of the special day celebrations are given but slight preliminary preparation and are limited to the immediate day when they occur in the school program, the teacher may not think it wise to introduce some of the songs until the day when they are to be used. This may make it desirable for the teacher alone to sing a song, with the children listening, or for the teacher to sing most of it and the children any little phrase which they can pick up quickly, such as the part given in the preceding section.

B. FOR TEACHER TO SING TO CHILDREN. 1. *America* (1 stanza). 2. *Battle Hymn of the Republic* (chorus only). 3. *Columbia, the Gem of the Ocean* (chorus). 4. *Hail Columbia* (chorus). 5. *The Strife Is O'er.*

The statements made in the preceding paragraph apply to the five songs listed here. Four of these are patriotic songs which may be sung at various times during the year, especially *America.* This old English tune was first sung with the American text in 1831 and was in current use in Lincoln's time. *Yankee Doodle,* presented under heading V-A 1, is the oldest of our tunes, dating back to the Revolutionary War. *Hail Columbia* was originally an instrumental number known as *The President's March,* in honor of Washington. The text was written in 1798. *Columbia, the Gem of the Ocean* was adapted to an English song early in the 19th century. *The Battle Hymn of the Republic* is connected with Lincoln and the Civil War. *The Strife is O'er* is a fine old Easter hymn, of which the children need sing only the three Alleluias— or possibly only the final one.

C. SUGGESTIONS FOR SINGERS. The variety of moods of the various celebrations included in this unit on Special Days may easily be used to stimulate the creative spirit in children. When it is evident that the children are greatly interested in some topic which is being discussed, they should be encouraged to consider it quietly for a moment or two and then, if they feel they have something which they would like to express to the rest of the group, to say it or sing it.

Sometimes the results will be merely the reproduction of a little poem or song which has already been taught to the group. But frequently, it will be an original expression.

Strange sounds and weird intervals may be the result, but if the child is actually expressing something that seems important to him, the teacher may well be content. The only criticism she needs to give, is an inquiry as to whether the child is satisfied with what he has given, that is to say, whether his expression is as lovely as what he was thinking about. Text and tone are to be judged now on the basis of their adequacy for what the child desired.

While young voices should always be light and with no sense of strain, this does not mean that children should always be told to sing softly. The spirit of the phrase or song determines the quality of tone. Voice building at this period should be accomplished through the spirit of play or of dramatic expression. When the child is singing a lullaby the singing will naturally be gentle and soothing, but when he is singing of a bright color, a valentine, a great hero, the fun of St. Patrick's Day, or a surprise for father or mother, the tones will be light but they will be bright and vigorous.

V. *Rhythmic Plays and Dramatizations*

A. SONGS. 1. *Yankee Doodle.* 2. *The Flora Dance.*

Although the early patriotic song, *Yankee Doodle,* is presented with one stanza of a childlike text which may be sung by the children, the music is given in an instrumental version with directions for an effective dance. Since it involves more complicated figures than we have used before, it may be wise to have it danced by only a few of the more capable children, or by visiting children from an upper grade.

On the other hand, the old English children's dance is so simple that all the children may participate.

B. SPECIAL INSTRUMENTAL MATERIAL: 1. *Soldiers' March*, Schumann. 2. *St. Patrick's Day*. 3. *The Girl I Left Behind Me*.

These two jolly Irish dance tunes which are widely known to adults will justify their existence in this unit if they are used merely as listening material in celebrating St. Patrick's Day. Frequently, however, Irish children or adults may be found who will be glad to dance to the tunes and thus add a further note of gaiety. If possible, they should be played on a violin. They, like the Schumann number, are excellent for marching.

VI. *Listening Material*

1. *Consolation* (first theme), Mendelssohn. 2. *Bridal Chorus* (first part), Wagner. 3. *Sky Rockets*, Rossman.

These three sharply contrasted numbers may be used respectively for a Memorial Day celebration; as an instrumental illustration of some child's story of a wedding which he has attended; and as a forward look to a celebration which will come after school closes, namely, Fourth of July.

VII. *Rhythm Band*

Using whatever toy instruments have been introduced by the time any particular special day is being celebrated, the children may provide rhythmic accentuations for material presented earlier in this unit, such as IV-B 3, 4, 5, and V-A 1.

III. CALLS AND MOTIVES
(from songs and U.S. Army Bugle Calls)

1. A Birthday Wish

Hap-py birth-day.

2. Happy New Year

The old year's done!

3. Valentine Questions

Who sends val-en-tines?

4. Battle Hymn of the Republic

Glo - ry, glo - ry, hal - le - lu - jah!

5. Hail, Columbia!

Hail, Co-lum-bia, hap-py land.

6. The Strife is O'er

Al - le - lu - ia.

7. The Flora Dance

I can dance the Flo - ra.

8. To the Colors (*When raising the flag*)

9. Assembly

10. Reveille

Fine

D. C. al fine

11. Taps

IV. SONGS

A. FOR CHILDREN TO SING

1. A Birthday Wish

2. The Birthday Party

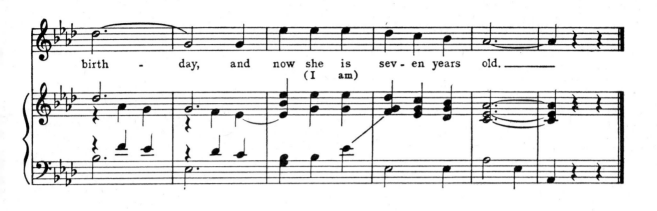

birth - day, and now she is sev- en years old. _____
(I am)

3. Happy New Year

Jane Landon

P. W. D.

Heavily, moderato

The old year's done, The old year's done! A ver-y hap-py New Year has just be- gun.

The accompaniment may be played an octave higher.

4. Our Flag

A. E.

Ann Engels

1. The flag that wears the stars and stripes, Is your flag and my flag.
2. This coun-try, our U - nit- ed States, Is your land and my land.

col 8va

5. For the Flag

1. Star-ry field of blue, Stripes of red and
2. Up a-bove the school, See the col-ors

white, The flag of our U-nit-ed States Is such a splen-did sight.
fly, The flag of our U-nit-ed States Is float-ing, proud and high.

6. About Abraham Lincoln

J. L.   P. W. D.

In martial time

A-bra-ham Lin-coln was good. A-bra-ham Lin-coln was

brave. Now for Lin-coln's birth-day the bright flags wave.

Ped. ※

7. Valentine Questions

J. L. V.   J. L. V.

1. Who sends val en-tines, Gay red val-en-tines? I sup-pose No one knows Who sends val en-tines.
2. Who gets val-en-tines, Gay red val-en-tines? Watch with me, Then we'll see Who gets val-en-tines

8 We Sing of Washington

J. L. V.   J L V

1. Good George Wash-ing-ton, great George Wash-ing-ton, Sing a hap-py song when his birth-day comes. Good George Wash-ing-ton, great George Wash-ing-ton, Sing a hap-py song with a beat of drums.
2. Good George Wash-ing-ton, great George Wash-ing-ton, Sing a hap-py song for his birth-day's here. Good George Wash-ing-ton, great George Wash-ing-ton, Sing a hap-py song with a rous-ing cheer.

9. The American Way

Margery Armitage

Samuel Drake

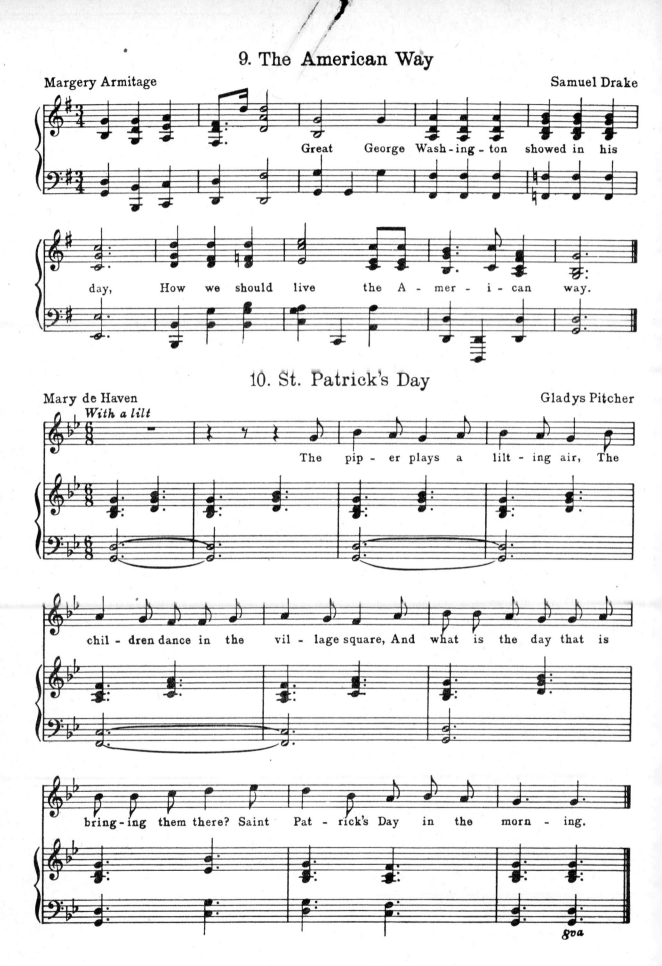

Great George Wash-ing-ton showed in his day, How we should live the A-mer-i-can way.

10. St. Patrick's Day

Mary de Haven

Gladys Pitcher

With a lilt

The pip-er plays a lilt-ing air, The chil-dren dance in the vil-lage square, And what is the day that is bring-ing them there? Saint Pat-rick's Day in the morn-ing.

8va

90

11. Easter Eggs

M. de H.

Mary de Haven

1. Eas-ter eggs, Eas-ter eggs, Pur-ple, red, and blue The pur-ple is for Moth-er, The red one is for you.
2. Can-dy eggs, can-dy eggs, Hid-den in a nest I like them made of can-dy, But real eggs are the best.

12. A Tune About Trees

J. L. V.

J. Lilian Vandevere

We're plant-ing a sap-ling for Ar-bor Day. A ti-ny thing as you can see. But still we know it's sure to grow, And make a love-ly tree._

13. The First of May

J.L.

Sarah Olds

1.Join the danc-ing in a
2.Hang May bas-kets on this

mer - ry ring,   Come and sing,   Form a ring.
glad May day,   Ring the bell,   Run a - way.

Join the dancing in a mer-ry ring,   This is the First of May.
Hang May bas-kets on this glad May day,   This is the First of May.

14. For Mother's Day

H. F.

Helen Fitch

I'm sing-ing for you A song that will say, "I love my dear moth-er this Moth-ers' Day."

92

15. For Father's Day

H. F.

William Peters

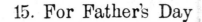

I'm sing-ing a Fa-ther's Day song you see For I love my Dad-dy, and he loves me.

B. FOR TEACHER TO SING TO CHILDREN

1. America
(My Country, 'Tis of Thee)

S. F. Smith

Henry Carey (?)

My coun-try 'tis of thee, Sweet land of lib-er-ty, Of thee I sing. Land where my fa-thers died! Land of the Pil-grim's pride! From ev-'ry moun-tain side, Let free-dom ring!

2. Battle Hymn of the Republic

Julia Ward Howe

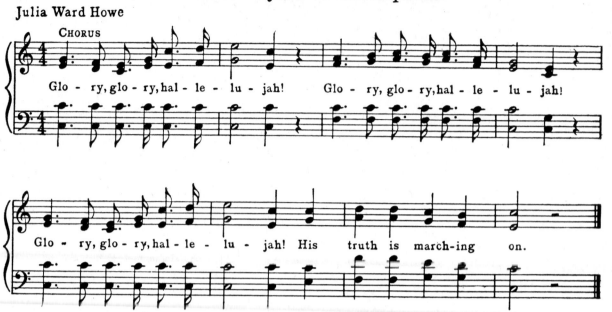

CHORUS

Glo - ry, glo - ry, hal - le - lu - jah! Glo - ry, glo - ry, hal - le - lu - jah!

Glo - ry, glo - ry, hal - le - lu - jah! His truth is march-ing on.

3. Columbia, the Gem of the Ocean

Origin uncertain

CHORUS

Three cheers for the red, white, and blue! Three

cheers for the red white and blue! The ar - my and na - vy for-

ev - er, Three cheers for the red, white and blue!

4. Hail, Columbia!

Joseph Hopkinson

The President's March by
Philip Phyle

Firm, u‑nit‑ed let us be, Ral‑lying round our lib‑er‑ty!

As a band of broth‑ers joined, Peace and safe‑ty we shall find.

5. The Strife is O'er

From the Latin. Tr. F. Potts (1861)

Arr. from Palestrina (1515-1594)

Al‑le‑lu‑ia! Al‑le‑lu‑ia! Al‑le‑lu‑ia!

The strife is o'er, the bat‑tle done, The vic‑to‑ry of life is

won; The song of tri‑umph has be‑gun. Al‑le‑lu‑ia!

V. RHYTHMIC PLAYS AND DRAMATIZATIONS

A. SONGS

1. Yankee Doodle

Introduction

Origin uncertain

This infectious little tune is excellent for rhythmic movement. We present two groups of suggestions, the first very simple, the other more involved.

A. As many children as desired march in a circle during the first eight measures, taking two steps to the measure. They stop for the chorus and, facing the center, clap their hands once to the measure six times alternating to the right and the left. For the other two measures they clap four times and turn around in their places.

(1) With partners in large circle march round the room during the verse. On the chorus join hands and (2) take 4 slides in the direction of the march, and (3) 4 slides back; (4) turn partner with six walking or skipping steps; (5) inside partner, with 2 steps advances to next player for new partner. Tune may be played by accompanist or may be sung with words, as printed below, by children who are not dancing.

Some frequently used texts

Early children's version

Father and I went down to camp
  Along with Captain Good'in,
And there we saw the men and boys
  As thick as hasty puddin'.
Chorus
Yankee Doodle keep it up
  Yankee Doodle dandy,
Mind the music and the step,
  And with the girls be handy.

Earlier adult version

Yankee Doodle went to town
  Riding on a pony,
Stuck a feather in his cap
  And called it macaroni.

2. The Flora Dance

1st time in slow walking tempo.
2nd time twice as fast, for skipping.

Old English Folk Dance
Arranged by P. W. D.

1. First of May's the Flo-ra's day. Can you dance the
BOTH 2. Tra la la la la la la la Tra la la la

Flo - ra? Yes, I can with a gen-tle-man I can dance the Flo - ra.
la la Tra la la la la la la la la Tra la la la la la la

Directions: Partners in two lines facing each other, ten or twelve feet apart. In first four measures of song, the head boy sings and walks half way to partner, making a bow in his final measure. In next four measures, the head girl sings and walks to partner, making a curtsy in her final measure. On the repetition, the partners join hands and skip down the lane, up, and down again, stopping at the bottom. The song is then repeated with the new head couple. The singing is done by all the children.

B. SPECIAL INSTRUMENTAL MATERIAL

1. Soldiers' March

Robert Schumann

97

2. St. Patrick's Day

Lively

Old Irish Air

3. The Girl I Left Behind Me
(The Rambling Laborer)

Old Irish Air

Moderato

VI. LISTENING MATERIAL

1. Consolation

Felix Mendelssohn

2. Wedding March

Richard Wagner
in *Lohengrin*

3. Sky Rockets

Floy Adele Rossman

Games, Rhythms and Plays

I Guiding Educational Principles

PLAY is now recognized as a powerful educational force. With children, at least, it is not merely fun, but an enterprise requiring thought and action guided by careful planning. Some philosophers go so far as to say that many kinds of play make as great demands upon the human being for organization and effort as work does. In fact, they maintain that frequently there is no difference between the efforts involved in play and in work except that the latter usually involves an onerous or forced sort of character. They maintain that the right sort of play has the highest educational significance.

Group-play involves important individual skills and co-operative adjustments. John Dewey writes "As the need for order is recognized, play becomes a game , it has 'rules.' There is also a gradual transition, such that play involves not only an ordering of activities toward an end but also an ordering of *materials*."

II Musical Applications

All music used by a group develops a type of communal play, because it involves constant adjustments of each individual to other individuals, if it be nothing more than keeping quiet while the others listen. Group rhythmic games and dances naturally require considerable adjustment of the participants. Many of these traditional musical expressions stem from children of centuries long past.

Learning and playing these games and rhythmic movements form a part of the heritage of the race which should not be denied to our present-day children simply because of the changes wrought by our civilization. The particular incidents and surroundings which are mentioned in these singing games no longer exist for many of our children, especially those who live in cities, but the instinctive urges which originally stimulated them are to a great extent still strong today.

The old games and the newer adaptations of them have repeatedly demonstrated that they are not only fun for the children of today but that they aid greatly in understanding the children and hence the people of other times and places.

In this unit, together with similar material included in other units, will be found something which is adapted for use on practically any school day. Singing and playing with rhythmic movements should be restored to its place as a natural and frequent expression of childhood.

III. Calls and Motives

1. *Hi, Spy.* 2. *Song of the Shoes.* 3. *Come, Dance.* 4. *Little Shadow.* 5. *Rowing.* 6. *Pinocchio Walks.* 7. *Pinocchio Skips.*

Talking with children about games which they play outside the school may disclose that there are calls used in summoning the players or in carrying out the game. Some of these may be suitable for tone or motive drills by the entire class as a group, or as individuals. We present a number of phrases from complete songs given later, which may be used either for their own sake, or as introductions to the songs.

IV. Songs

A. FOR CHILDREN TO SING. 1. *Hi, Spy.* 2. *Marching.* 3. *Changing Partners.* 4. *Song of the Shoes.* 5. *Come, Dance.* 6. *Little Shadow.* 7. *Heel and Toe.* 8. *Lightly Trip It.* 9. *Rowing.* 10. *Pinocchio Walks.* 11. *Pinocchio Skips.* 12. *Counting the Days.* 13. *How They Dance.*

Practically all the material in this unit has been selected for its adaptability as stimulating rhythmic music. Many of the songs, however, may be sung if desired without action. Those listed above are this type. The singing may come either before or after the song is used for rhythmic movements. When action is used, it is preferable to have only a portion of the children participate in it while the others sing the song. Material from other units may be used to supplement the game songs presented here.

B. FOR TEACHER TO SING TO CHILDREN. 1. *Dutch Boys.* 2. *Fiesta.* 3. *Puppets.*

These three songs will probably be too difficult for many of the children to sing, but they will enjoy listening when the teacher sings them. Moreover, after a number of the brighter children have heard the teacher sing them several times, they will probably try to join with her or even to sing them alone.

C. SUGGESTIONS FOR SINGERS. Whether or not the child sings in connection with his rhythmic plays and games, his breathing and the control of his body should be as free and natural as it is in good singing. In rhythmic plays there should be no rigid demands for precision of movement from the class, thus disregarding individual rhythm. The length and contour of a rhythmic wave is in proportion to the size of the body moved. Hence, while the class moves as a unit, each child will give something different or individual, even with the same general type of rhythm.

For the teacher, the all-important thing is to see that all spines are long and that the heads float over them. This overcomes stiffness of neck and jaw. The feeling of lightness should permeate all movements, especially marching. The three conditions to be considered at all times are, long spine, floating head, and broad back. A broad back means that the shoulders are not tautly drawn backward, but are allowed to fall naturally in place.

Rhythmic movement should be carried on by suggestions rather than by commands. The children should strive to express their own impressions, rather than blindly do what they are told. But even when some commands seem necessary they should *not* include the following which are still too frequently given to little children:

(1) Stand as tall as you can. (2) Pull shoulders back. (3) Draw abdomen in. (4) Draw chin in. (5) Stand with knees drawn back. (6) Place or hold some particular part of the body in a certain fixed position.

V. *Rhythmic Plays and Dramatizations*

A. SINGING GAMES. 1. *Action Song.* 2. *Galloping.* 3. *Making Music.* 4. *The Puppet Play.* 5. *Fingers Dance.*

These five songs, which are helped greatly by having accompanying action, are even simpler than those which are given in IV-A.

B. SPECIAL INSTRUMENTAL MATERIAL. 1. *Flourish of Trumpets,* Mendelssohn. 2. *Scotch Dance,* Beethoven. 3. *Captain Jinks,* Early American. 4. *Butterfly Motive,* Cator. 5. *Hide and Seek,* Loomis. 6. *Ballet from Rosamund,* Schubert. 7. *Skipping Dance,* Bentley.

These seven compositions, having neither words nor specific directions, may be used for original bodily expression by the children. In general this should be stimulated by using the pieces for a time as listening material only. When the children are thoroughly familiar with a piece and express a desire to dance or make other bodily movements with it, three or four children may be allowed to show what they would do. After all those who have ideas have demonstrated them, the entire group, through discussion, may select those which are to serve for the rhythmic expression of the class as a whole.

VI. *Listening*

No additional material is presented in this unit under this heading because suggestions for using preceding material have already been given.

VII. *Rhythm Band*

1. *Our Band.*

This little play song may be used for review and to increase the number of kinds of instruments used. These same instruments may be used with the following selections already presented in this unit: IV-A 2, drum and cymbals; IV-A 4, woodblock; IV-A 6, triangle; IV-B 1, woodblock; IV-B 2, tambourine; V-B 3, triangle; V-B 4, triangle, woodblock and tambourine; V-B 5, woodblock, triangle and drum.

III. CALLS AND MOTIVES

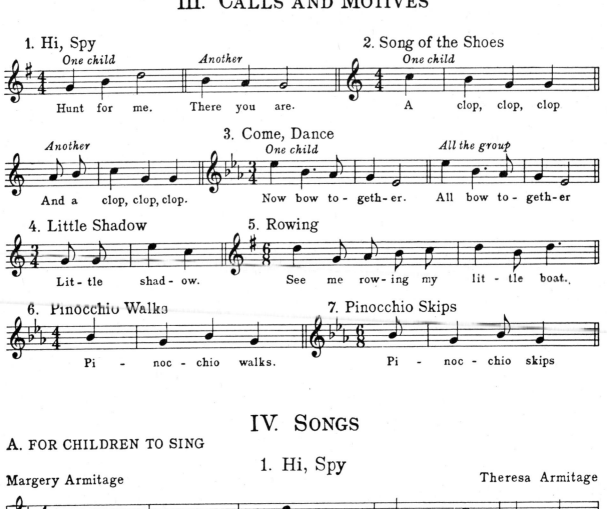

1. Hi, Spy

One child — Hunt for me. *Another* — There you are.

2. Song of the Shoes

One child — A clop, clop, clop.

3. Come, Dance

Another — And a clop, clop, clop. *One child* — Now bow to-geth-er. *All the group* — All bow to-geth-er.

4. Little Shadow

Lit-tle shad-ow.

5. Rowing

See me row-ing my lit-tle boat.

6. Pinocchio Walks

Pi-noc-chio walks.

7. Pinocchio Skips

Pi-noc-chio skips

IV. SONGS

A. FOR CHILDREN TO SING

1. Hi, Spy

Margery Armitage

Theresa Armitage

1 I am hid-ing one, two, three! Hi, Spy,
2 Now you have to hide from me! Hi, Spy,

hunt for me! I am not so ver-y far,— Hi, Spy, there you are
one, two, three I shall try to find you too,— Hi, Spy, I see you

2. Marching

T. A.

English Folk Tune
Accomp. by P. W. D.

Marching, march-ing, here they come, March-ing to the big bass drum;

Kate and Har-ry, Tom and Ma-ry March-ing to the drum.

3. Changing Partners

Swedish Folk Tune
Accomp. by T. A.

Adapted

Some-one took my lit-tle part-ner, I must find an-oth-er one.
I'll take you if you will have me, We will dance till day is done.

I have, tra la la, I have, tra la la, I have, tra la la, I have won!

4. Song of the Shoes

Dutch Folk Tune
Arranged by F. A. R.

A clop, clop, clop and a
clop, clop, clop, the wood - en shoes sing a song. A
clop, clop, clop, and a clop, clop, clop, the whole day long.

5. Come, Dance

Swedish Folk Tune
Arranged by T. A.

Come let us dance a - round, a - round, Oh let us dance a -

104

round, a-round. Oh come let us dance a-round, a-round, And

then a bow to our part-ner. All bow to-geth-er

6. Little Shadow

E. A.

Elizabeth Allen

Lit-tle shad-ow, lit-tle shad-ow, Now a dance let us

try, Lit-tle shad-ow, lit-tle shad-ow, You and I, you and I.

7. Heel and Toe

Olive Woodman

Mary Root Kern

1. Heel and toe and one, two, three, Whirl and twirl and clap with me. Spright-ly, light-ly, gay and free, Danc-ing in the sun

2 Heel and toe and on we go, Fid-dler, fid-dler, why so slow? Hop and skip and point the toe, Danc-ing in the sun

8. Lightly Trip It

T. A.

Russian Folk Tune
Arranged by T. A.

Very slowly

Nod to the left, nod to the right, First we bow, then we turn a-bout.

Come, my part-ner, light-ly trip it, Light-ly trip it in a ring.
Come, my part-ner, light-ly trip it, Light-ly trip it as we sing.

Directions: Children form double circle, facing partners. Nod, bow, and turn, as directed in music. On chorus, partners join hands, and run forward with small light steps. At close of chorus inner circle moves to right, giving each player a new partner.

9. Rowing

F. A. R.

Floy Adele Rossman

1. See me row-ing my lit-tle boat,
2. See me row-ing my lit-tle boat,

Row-ing o-ver the sea.____ See me row-ing my lit-tle boat, No
See me pull-ing the oar.____ See me row-ing a-way to sea, And

sails at all for me.____
back a-gain to shore.____

10. Pinocchio Walks

H. S.

Harriet Storrs

Andante

sempre staccato

Pi - noc - chio walks, clop,
clop, clop, clop, clop, clop, clop, clop, clop, clop.

11. Pinocchio Skips

H S

H.S.

Allegro

Pi - noc - chio skips, clip -
clop, clip - clop, clip - clop, clip - clop, clip - clop.

12. Counting the Days

Translated

Bahama Islands Folk Tune
Arranged by T.A.

1. This is Mon - day morn - ing
2. This is Tues - day morn - ing } ta - ma ta - ma
3. This is Wednes - day morn - ing } *etc.*

13. How They Dance

French Folk Tune
Accomp. by J. L. V.

J. L. V.

1. In the land of Hol-land, that is far a-cross the
2. In the land of Rus-sia, that is far a-cross the
3. In the land of Eng-land, that is far a-cross the

o-cean, Hap-py lit-tle chil-dren dance a mer-ry dance.
o-cean, Hap-py lit-tle chil-dren dance a mer-ry dance.
o-cean, Hap-py lit-tle chil-dren dance a mer-ry dance. DANCE

(The children improvise

steps)

tam,____ Whoo - oo ta - ma ta - ma tam.____

1. Dutch Boys

S.B.

Stephene Blake

Intro.

Not too fast

The Dutch boys are
whis-t'ling a lit-tle mer-ry tune. Their wood-en shoes clop to the
lit-tle mer-ry tune. Clop, clop, clop, clop, clop, clop, clop, clop, clop, clop. They
dance and they whis-tle the lit-tle mer-ry tune.

2. Fiesta

Sidney Rowe

Mexican Song
Arranged by Gladys Pitcher

CHORUS

Pupils may join with teacher.

Tir - a - lir - a - li, tir - a - lir - a - li, tir - a - lir - a - le - ra __

__ Tir - a - lir - a - li, tir - a - lir - a - li, tir - a - lir - a - le - ra. __

__ There is laugh - ter and song And a light - heart - ed

throng 'Neath the bright sil - ver light of the moon. __

3. Puppets

F. A. R.

Floy Adele Rossman

See the mer-ry pup-pets in a sway-ing row, Step-ping oh, so light-ly on each

dain-ty toe. Ev-'ry sau-cy head is nod-ding to and fro.

They are mer-ry pup-pets from a pup-pet show.

V. RHYTHMIC PLAYS AND DRAMATIZATIONS

A SINGING GAMES

1 Action Song

Old Singing Game

Let your feet tramp tramp let your hands clap, clap, And each one make a bow.

(Choose partner)

(Children skip with chosen partner.)

And each one make a bow.

2. Galloping

A. E.

Ann Engels

A - gal - lop a - way, a - gal - lop a - way, My hob-by-horse gal-lops to mar-ket to-day O - ver the bridge and in - to the town, A - gal-lop-ing, gal-lop-ing up and down.

The rhythm of the hobby horse is imitated by placing one foot a bit ahead of the other, keeping the knees flexed and the body balanced to accomodate the backward and forward swing.

A desired adaptability to change of tempo is gained by dramatization. A Fairy Queen inspects her slowly moving hobby-horses. She has the power to change them to live ponies. As she touches each head with her wand, the music is quickened and each little horse is free to gallop on his way. As the ponies once more approach the Queen, she touches them with her wand, the music changes and the hobby horses resume their slow-moving balance.

114

3. Making Music

Italian Folk Tune
Arranged by F A R.

T.A.

(1-4) If you wish, I'll play a tune on my

(1) vi - o - lin for you, Hm ___
(2) pic - co - lo for you, Toot - le too - too - toot - le, toot - le - too - too -
(3) big bass drum for you, Pr - rum, pum, pum, pum, pum, pum, pum, pum, pum,
(4) tam - bour - ine for you, Chink, chink, chink, chink, chink, chink, chink, chink, chink,

too Toot - le too - too - toot - le, toot - le - too - too - too.
pum. Pr - rum, pum, pum, pum, pum, pum, pum, pum, pum, pum.
chink Chink, chink, chink, chink, chink, chink, chink, chink, chink, chink.

115

4. The Puppet Play

Helen Fitch

French Folk Tune
Accomp. by H.F.

1. Come and see our show. Watch the pup-pets ca-per through it. It is good, we know, And we're giv-ing it to-day.
2. Pup-pets jump and run. You will laugh to see them do it. We made ev-'ry one, And we hope you like the play.

5. Fingers Dance

Traditional

Tyrolean Folk Song
Arranged by T.A.

Come dance lit-tle Thumb-kin, Point-er, Tall-man, Gold-ie, Ba-by, Come dance and be mer-ry, The chil-dren are mer-ry, So dance and be gay.

B. SPECIAL INSTRUMENTAL MATERIAL

PHILOSTRATE: So please your Grace, the Prologue is address'd.

THESEUS: Let him approach.

1. Flourish of Trumpets

Felix Mendelssohn
in *Midsummer Night's Dream*

This may be used as introduction to many little dramatic scenes, or as a prologue to a puppet play.

2. Scotch Dance

Ludwig van Beethoven
Arranged by F.A.R.

117

3. Captain Jinks

Early American Tune

4. Butterfly Motive

Thomas Vincent Cator
in *Inchling*

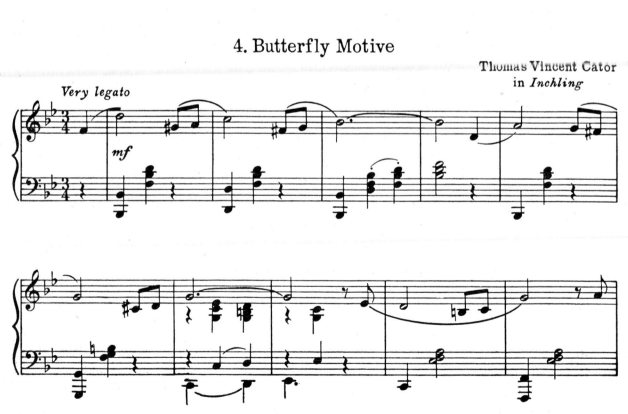

5. Hide and Seek

Harvey Worthington Loomis

6. Ballet from Rosamunde

Franz Schubert

7. Skipping Dance

Alys Bentley

VII. Rhythm Band

1. Our Band

J. L. V.

French Folk Tune
Accomp. by W. P.

1. I play on my tam-bour-ine,
2. I play on my lit-tle drum,
3. I play on my wood-block too,
4. The tri-an-gle's tone is clear,
5. The cym-bals are loud and strong,

Let me show you how I play.
Let me show you how I play.
Let me show you how I play. how I play.
Let me show you how I play.
Let me show you how I play.

Rap and make it jin-gle,
Rub-a-dub I'm beat-ing
First I light-ly tap it,
Strike to set it ring-ing,
Just like this I clash them,

Shake and make it tin-gle.
Then I keep re-peat-ing.
Then I loud-ly rap it.
Strike to set it sing-ing.
Just like this I crash them.

Ho! Hi! Hey! Such an eas-y thing to play.

Music of American Indians

I. Guiding Educational Principles

THE study of primitive peoples has an established place in the curriculum of the elementary school, both because it is naturally interesting to the child and because it serves as an illuminating introduction to the complex life in which he lives. Nature-people who have no houses, wear little clothing, and who live almost entirely on what grows wild in and on the earth, rather than on what they cultivate, are easily understood by children

The intellectual and emotional life of primitive folk strikes a responsive chord in the young developing child. He takes the words and actions of these far-away people very seriously and can thus easily be led to imitate a way of life and habits of thinking and feeling which are frequently unwelcome when baldly presented as precepts for conduct today.

The North American Indian is a model which children gladly imitate, not only in our country, but in many other lands. This natural interest has great educational values.

II. Musical Applications

Our children readily sense the now well established fact that to the American Indian music was a medium between himself and the unseen Great Spirit. He lived his songs. He had a characteristic song for every important occasion, every significant phase of his life. His music brought about definite results within himself as he tried to adjust his own rhythm to vibrate with that of the universe.

Words and music, music and the dance, music and drama, music and religion, all were one and inseparable to the Indians. To quote Hartley Alexander, concerning the Indian's music, "It is not an outer reflection of life, but an integral cause."

Our use of Indian music stresses the general melodic and rhythmic feeling of the tune, because translations of the words lose much of the simplicity, beauty, and meaning of the original text. But the animating spirit which brought this music into existence still is potent. If our interpretations are sincere and natural, as children always tend to make them, our groups will quickly catch the serious and dignified character which they embody. Well chosen and wisely used Indian music can move children deeply.

III. Calls and Motives

1. *Corn Song.* 2. *Medicine Song.* 3. *Hunting Song.* 4. *Warrior.* 5. *Battle Cry.* 6. *Dance.*

So much of the Indian's music consisted of only one or two phrases repeated over and over that it is sometimes difficult to distinguish calls or motives from complete songs. Several modern American composers have utilized this idea by writing songs which are the development or extension of an Indian motive or call (e.g., MacDowell's *To A Wild Rose, From an Indian Lodge;* Cadman's *From the Land of the Sky Blue Water;* Lieurance's *By the Waters of Minnetonka;* Gaines' *Out Where the West Begins*). The calls given above may be supplemented by others drawn from songs presented in the next section. In fact, an excellent method for teaching most Indian songs is to have the children learn as a separate call the principal motive on which the song is written.

IV, V, VI. Songs, Rhythmic Plays and Dramatizations, Listening Material

Since practically all Indian music, whether sung or played, was accompanied by bodily movement, we shall not separate the various phases of music as we usually do in these units. Instead, we shall accompany almost every composition with a special note indicating particular uses.

IV. A. SONGS FOR CHILDREN TO SING. 1. *Blue Corn Grinding Song*, Zuni. 2. *Medicine Song*, Apache. 3. *My Owlet*, Kiowa. 4. *Indian Warriors*, Arapahoe. 5. *Pipe of Peace*, Arapahoe. 6. *The Navajo Weaver*, Navajo.

B. SONGS FOR TEACHER TO SING TO CHILDREN (who listen only or act the text.) 1. *Greeting*, Passamaquoddy. 2. *Rain Song*, Yuma. 3. *Hunting Song*, Ojibway. 4. *Hunting the Deer*, Navajo. 5. *The Cradle on the Bough*, Omaha.

These songs should be taught only with the use of the voice and the drum. Piano accompaniments are necessarily harmonic, and should be used later only, for the background to support or as program assistance.

V and VI. RHYTHMIC PLAYS AND DRAMATIZATIONS; LISTENING MATERIAL.

1. *To the Rising Sun*, Chippewa. 2. *Cradle Song*, Kwakiutl. 3. *Farewell to the Warriors*, Chippewa. 4. *Indian Song-Dance*, Dakota. 5. *Follow the Leader*, Ojibway. 6. *Corn Chant*, Dakota. 7. *Chant of the Crows*, Chippewa.

The common rhythm is the even or two-beat measure. But when the accent reveals a three, four, five, or even seven-beat measure in the same dance, the interpretation continues to be an even movement of the body. The accent is indicated in the heavier beat of the drum, and the sharper accent — heavier step — of the dancer.

Rhythms commonly used are:

123

III. INDIAN CALLS AND MOTIVES

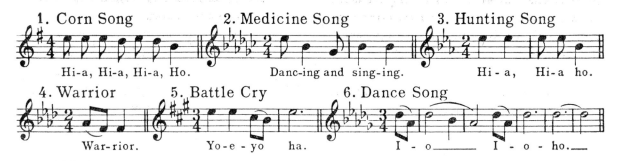

1. Corn Song — Hi-a, Hi-a, Hi-a, Ho.
2. Medicine Song — Danc-ing and sing-ing.
3. Hunting Song — Hi-a, Hi-a ho.
4. Warrior — War-rior.
5. Battle Cry — Yo-e-yo ha.
6. Dance Song — I-o I-o-ho.

IV. SONGS

A. FOR CHILDREN TO SING

The Zuni Indians raise beautiful blue, red, yellow and white corn of which they are very proud. They live in houses, and the grinding stone for their corn is firmly set into the floor and surrounded with stone gutters to receive the ground meal. The corn is placed on the stone and ground by rubbing another stone over it. Then the meal is swept up with a small brush into a basket, and later placed in large decorated pottery jars.

Women grind the corn, and always sing as they work. They kneel and sway back and forth with a rhythmic swing as they move the stone. If the workers are young girls, young men usually are standing about the room singing the song or playing upon flutes and drums.

CEREMONY OF CORN GRINDING

Two Indian girls place small blankets upon the floor, one for each worker, with a flat and a grinding stone in the center of each blanket. These blankets form a circle.

The workers enter in single file to the music of the verses, each carrying a flat basket on her left hip and a small brush made of a cluster of reeds in her right hand. The jars are carried on the top of the head and supported by the right arm. The jar bearers follow the workers. The girls take their places in front of the stones while the bearers of the jars stand on either side of the circle, facing the audience.

The Indian boys follow the girls, and stand in a group at the back or sit at the drums at one side of the circle. They sing the song.

During the verses, the girls grind their corn. During each prelude, the brushes are picked up and the meal rhythmically swept into the baskets. At the close of the last verse, the girls rise and lift the baskets high with both hands, and with upturned faces offer silent thanksgiving to the Great Spirit (eight measures). As the music continues, the jar bearers pass to each worker and the baskets are slowly emptied. Then the two jar bearers again lift them to their heads and lead the workers, bearing their baskets as before, from the room. The boys follow, the drummers continuing, however, until all others have gone.

1. Blue Corn-Grinding Song

J. L.

Zuni
Accomp. by F. A. R.

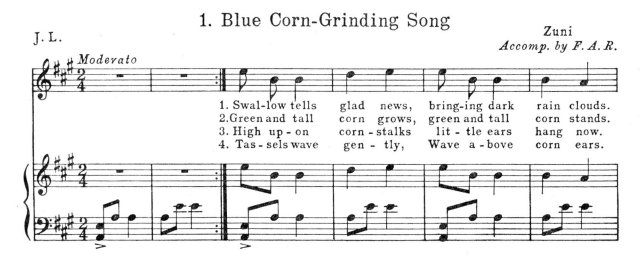

Moderato

1. Swal-low tells glad news, bring-ing dark rain clouds.
2. Green and tall corn grows, green and tall corn stands.
3. High up-on corn-stalks lit-tle ears hang now.
4. Tas-sels wave gen-tly, Wave a-bove corn ears.

Hi - ya - ho, Hi - ya - ho, Hi - ya - he.

The Apaches have their home in New Mexico and Arizona. Geronimo was their most famous war leader. He was also a Medicine Man and was called Holy Man by his people, whom he greatly loved. He believed that the Great Spirit gave him his songs of healing. What we print is a small part of one which was constantly used in the healing ceremony.

The young medicine man wears a simple feather-decorated head dress that has two buffalo horns, curving out and upward, over each temple. He carries a medicine stick, a feather dangling from its tip. It may be about two feet long with two short cross bars placed diagonally near the top.

The dance is a simple step, a slow and stately movement, to the beat of the drum, about the circle of seated braves. If the circle is large enough to permit it, a sick brave lies in the center. As the braves dance about him, the medicine stick, always held in the right hand, is rhythmically shaken over the sick man so that its healing power may fall upon him.

2. Medicine Song

F. A. R.

Apache
Sung by Geronimo
Accomp. by F. A. R.

Slowly, with dignity

Danc-ing and sing-ing, Danc-ing and sing-ing,

Danc-ing and sing-ing, We heal the sick brave, sick brave. Hi!
(spoken)

The word "owlet" is a very popular term of endearment with the Indian mother.

She carefully straps her baby into his cradle and fastens it on her back. As she softly croons the lullaby, she sways, bending forward and back. There is usually a rhythmic pattern to her movements, every other forward bend being a bit lower than the first.

Very soon the little black eyes of the baby close in sleep.

3. My Owlet

F.A.R.

Kiowa
Accomp. by F.A.R.

With a slow swing

Owl-et, my owl-et is sleep - ing.

Wee stars are twink-ling in the sky.
Moth - er is sing-ing lul - la - by.

In this next dance there must be space for a large sized circle. Place the drummers and gourd shakers at one side of the circle, with the Indian women back of these. The women hum the song along with the musicians who carry the singing of the verses. The dancers themselves need not sing.

Both the double-beat step (described in the Ojibway Hunting Song) and the step called the Toe-Heel or Toe-Flat step are common to warrior dances.

The Toe-Heel step, in four-beat measure, is as follows,—

       1. One step forward on left toe,

       2. Drop left heel in place.

       3. Step forward on right toe,

       4. Drop right heel in place.

The body sways at each complete step; the arms are bent at the elbow and the hands keep time to the drumbeat.

4. Indian Warrior

F.A.R.

Arapahoe
Accomp. by F. A. R.

I'm an In-dian war-rior, war-rior, Big Chief In-dian
On my back a quiv-er, quiv-er, Full of man-y

war-rior, war-rior.
ar-rows, ar-rows. (continue dance)

I'm an In-dian war-rior, war-rior, Big Chief In-dian war-rior, war-rior,

Hi - Ho! Hi - Ho! Hi.
(shouted lightly)

The American Indian is the only race known to use the ceremony of a peace pipe, with the mysteries of all rites of incense rising to the gods.

In the ceremony, the Chief is seated on the council rock. In front of him is the council fire, and facing him in a semi-circle, are the Indian men. Directly opposite is the Medicine Man. To the right, the drummers, and to the left sitting silently with shawls over their heads, are the Indian women.

The Chief rises and calls to a member standing near, "Pipe bearer, bring to me our Pipe of Peace."

The bearer approaches, carrying the pipe in his outstretched hands. He lays it in the outstretched hands of the Chief who raises it up and lifts his head, saying "Great Spirit, we come in peace about the council fire. We smoke our pipe that there be more peace."

The Chief nears the fire, reaches for a small brand and lights the pipe. He returns to his place, seats himself, and smokes as the men sing. He hands the pipe to the brave on his right, who takes a short puff, and hands it on. The music continues until all have smoked the pipe and it returns to the hands of the Chief. He again rises in his place, and the council rises, while the Chief again lifts the pipe and repeats his prayer to the Great Spirit.

The Chief hands the pipe to the bearer, folds his arms across his chest, and strides away, followed by the bearer, the Medicine Man, the braves, and lastly, the Indian women.

5. Pipe of Peace

F. A. R.

Arapahoe
Accomp. by F. A. R.

Slowly, with dignity

Our pipe of peac we smoke to-day. Our pipe of peace we smoke to-day. (*The pipe is slowly passed and smoked, in pantomime.*)

6. The Navajo Weaver

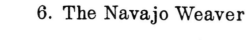

H. F.

Navajo
Accomp. by H. W. Loomis

I'm a bus-y Na-va-jo weav-er, Back and forth my

fin-gers fly. Then, when my rugs are fin-ished, Man-y white men come to buy.

B. SONGS FOR TEACHER TO SING TO CHILDREN
(who listen only, or act the text)

1. Greeting

F. A. R.

Passamaquoddy
Accomp. by F. A. R.

Slowly, with dignity

Wel-come, wel-come, my friends to the wig - wam.

He - ga, He-ga.___ He - ga - ne he. Hi!
(spoken)

The braves sit in a circle with heads bent and arms folded. The Indian women sit back of the circle: shawls cover their faces and they sway from side to side and softly sing. At no time do the women sing loudly. Often they croon the tune through open lips.

The players use a muffled drum and dried gourds or dried skins filled with pebbles.

2. Rain Song

Yuma

Transcribed by and accomp. by F. A. R.

H. F.

1. Hear, Great Spir-it, corn is dy-ing. Hear, Great Spir-it, corn is dy-ing.
2. Hear, Great Spir-it, send us rain clouds Hear, Great Spir-it, send us rain clouds.

A-wah!__ A-wah!__ A-wah!__ A-wah!__ Hi!
(spoken softly)

This dance may use the double-beat step. In this, short steps are always taken. The entire foot is placed on the floor for beat one, then the heel is raised and it lightly taps the floor for beat two. The knees are slightly bent, with the arms jerkily carrying the rhythm of the beat.

The young hunter, armed with bow and arrow searches for his game. He rhythmically lifts the bow to aim high on the hill-top, or again to point low over the plain. While the dance steps are in perfect unison to the beat of the drum, the interpretation of the hunting is wholly individual.

The dance usually is in a circle, or for a single line of hunters.

3. Hunting Song

F. A. R

Ojibway
Accomp. by F. A. R.

Hi ya, Hi - ya, Hi - ya,

Hi - ya-ho. We will go a - hunt - ing the car - i - bou. Hi - ya, Hi - ya,

Hi - ya, Hi - ya-ho. We will go a - hunt - ing the car - i - bou. Hi!
(spoken)

In the early days before the Navajos became shepherds, they lived by hunting. All the hunters knew the songs given them by Hastyealti, the god of sunrise and wild game. Before going to the hunt, they gathered together, praying to the god and singing his song. The god always answered those who were sincere in the song.

As each hunter went to the woods, he stood immovable in his place chanting the song. The deer, fascinated by the chant and fulfilling the promise of the god, went directly to the hunter.

The young hunters, bearing bows and arrows, stand or kneel in readiness for the approaching game. They chant the song quietly and with monotonous rhythm until the end of the song when the arrow is let loose and each hunter runs to examine his game. Then he stands, raises both hands to the Great Spirit of the Chase, and again softly chants the first verse in thanksgiving.

The drums are placed on one side of the room away from the hunters. Drumsticks are muffled with padding to give the impression of distance.

4. Hunting the Deer

F. A. R.

Navajo
Accomp. by F. A. R.

1. Comes the deer to my singing,
2. Light and swift is my ar-row,

Comes the deer to my song, Comes the deer to my sing-ing, i - ne - ya.
Tight and strong is my bow, Light and swift is my ar-row, i - ne - ya.

5. The Cradle on the Bough

H. F.

Omaha
Accomp. by H. W. Loomis

Small pa-poose in your cra-dle nest, Breez-es blow to

132

rock you and give you sleep and rest, sleep and rest. Small pa-poose in your

cra - dle nest, Breez-es blow to rock you and give you sleep and rest.

V & VI. RHYTHMIC PLAYS AND DRAMATIZATIONS: LISTENING MATERIAL

This composition may be used merely for listening or as music to accompany a pantomime of greeting the sun.

1. To the Rising Sun

(A flute call)

Chippewa Ceremonial
Arranged by F. A. R.

This cradle song may be used merely for listening and as accompanying music in a pantomime or little play, or it may be hummed or sung with the word Ha-o by the children.

The Kwakiutl Indians live along the northwest coast, and many have built their homes on the island of Vancouver, B.C. The tribe possesses unusual culture and exhibits a rare skill in the carving of totem poles. Their music is full of the spirit of mystery, and yet often suggests the even beat of the sea. There is rare beauty in their melodies.

The Kwakiutls live in wooden houses, and the mother often hangs the cradle of her baby from a cross beam in the corner of the house. She attaches a cord to the cradle and rocks her baby to and fro as she croons. There is only one word to the cradle song, Ha-o, which means, Sleep-o.

2. Cradle Song

Kwakiutl
Arranged by F. A. R.

This is a very old song of the Chippewas. At the time of war, as the fighting men were marching away, the Indian women slowly walked behind their braves, singing the farewell song. They halted at the edge of the village, softly singing until the warriors were out of sight, then still singing, they returned alone to their wigwams.

As given here, the song is treated as a flute solo. It may be used for quiet listening, or as music to accompany pantomime.

3. Farewell to the Warriors

Chippewa
Arranged by F. A R

This dance gives a fine opportunity for the use of Indian drums and rattles. The children may make drums from cylindrical cereal boxes, covering them with paper, and decorating them with Indian designs in paint, crayons, or cut paper.

A large drum may be made from a cheese box or a cardboard hat box. Such a drum may be played by using the two hands alternately in each measure.

The drums with the heaviest tone may be used as tom-toms, the players beating with their hands on the two ends of the drum. If the piano part of this tune is played properly, all the children will feel a stronger stroke on the first beat of each measure.

Rattles may be made by filling dried gourds or small boxes with pebbles. These rattles may play the rhythm of four eighth-notes in a measure. A particularly musical child may follow the rhythm of the melody.

The dancers may use the toe-heel step described on page 126, or improvise their own steps. Children who feel the rhythm keenly may shake rattles and dance at the same time.

4. Indian Dance

Dakota
Arranged by J. L.

5. Follow the Leader
(Children's Game)

Ojibway
Arranged by P. W. D.

Worn out are my shoes of deer-skin, Worn out are my shoes of
Mu-je mu-ke-sin au-yaw-yon. Mu-je mu-ke-sin au-

deer-skin, Worn out are my shoes of deer-skin, Worn out are my shoes of deer-skin.
yaw-yon. Mu-je mu-ke-sin au-yaw-yon. Mu-je mu-ke-sin au-yaw-yon.

6. Corn Chant

Dakota

Rhythmic drum pattern: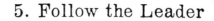

These words are softly chanted, not sung to the beat of a drum.

Single rows of warriors and Indian women face each other.

As the drum beats a prelude, heads are slowly lifted to gaze upward. While chanting the first phrase, the left hand is lifted and held while the second phrase is sung and the right hand raised. The hands approach each other during the third phrase, then are slowly lowered, the eyes following the movement of the hands

> *Over cornfield comes the rain cloud,*
> *Over cornfield comes the thunder*
> *Butterflies will soon be playing*
> *Over corn with tassels waving.*

7. Chant of the Crows

Chippewa

A young man was fasting in his teepee. A flock of crows was in flight. The young man heard the crows and thought he understood what they said.

> *Among the birds that come in spring,*
> *I am the first to bring the rain.*
> *My name is Crow. I come in spring;*
> *I am the first to bring the rain.*

The words are spoken softly to the steady beat of the drum. The drum prelude is four measures.

136

The Country and Things to Eat

I. Guiding Educational Principles

WE have already, in Unit One, dealt with the country as a place for a vacation and we shall return to that idea later in our spring and summer units. But the child should also think of the country as a place from which come food, clothing, and many other necessities of life. The farmer is an indispensable friend and helper for the city dweller.

Even though many children cannot get to know intimately the activities of the farm, they are interested in the animals which are found there and the food which comes from there. They can quickly be led to understand how dependent city-dwellers are upon the country and its people. Likewise, they can easily grasp how the country dwellers make use of the products of the city. They are thus started on the conception that they will meet many times in their later lives, of the interdependence of town and country.

II. Musical Applications

All of the above ideas have been attractively expressed in both vocal and instrumental music, in the folk songs and games of the people and in compositions of known writers. For the children, of course, we shall select only the simpler and happier pieces.

The ease with which these are sung or acted or danced and the frequent appearance of the ideas of the texts in other activities or studies of the school program should often lead to the use of this material in periods other than those definitely set aside for music. The general application of this idea to all the various phases of the school program would not only heighten the interest in all periods but would also distribute advantageously throughout the day the talents of especially gifted children in various fields. We need to recognize the distinctively different powers of children not only in music but in all subjects of study.

Moreover, the strongly rhythmic character of much of the folk music indicates that the tendency of children to dramatize or dance their songs and games is one that is natural and beneficial. Allowing music of this and other units to be introduced at appropriate times during the school day will not only strengthen the individuality of the children, and thus foster the creative impulse, but will stimulate the children to use school music much more often outside the school.

III. Calls and Motives

1. *Quack, Quack, Quack.* 2. *The Cow.* 3. *Dinner Time.* 4. *Fol-de-rol-de-ri-do.* 5. *Rice.* 6. *My Gingerbread Man.* 7. *Baby Duck.* 8. *Counting Out.* 9. *Shepherd's Song* (*Pastoral Symphony*, Beethoven).

All of this material is drawn from compositions which appear later in the Unit — the first seven in songs and the last two in instrumental numbers. Short though they are, some of them, such as numbers two and three, may be still further divided by allowing various children to sing only one or two measures, the teacher or a child responding with the rest of the motive. This will help continue the play spirit and make these tone drills enjoyable even for children who have difficulty in singing correctly.

IV. Songs

A. FOR CHILDREN TO SING. 1. *Song of the Corn.* 2. *The Cow.* 3. *The Little Red Calf.* 4. *Dinner Time.* 5. *Quack, Quack, Quack.* 6. *Fol-de-rol-de-ri-do.* 7. *Take Your Choice!* 8. *The*

Milk Train. 9. *Rice.* 10. *Which?* 11. *My Gingerbread Man.* 12. *Mister Farmer.*

The first six songs have to do with the sights and activities of the farm, the remaining six with things to eat. Many of the songs lend themselves to dramatization and rhythmic activity. Children should be encouraged to devise their own interpretations.

B. FOR TEACHER TO SING TO CHILDREN. 1. *A Chicken's Ways.* 2. *Baby Duck.* 3. *The Barnyard Song.* 4. *Farmyard Song,* Grieg.

After a few hearings, some of the more capable children will probably be able to sing parts or all of these four songs. The teacher should welcome their participation after they have a good idea of the complete song and ask to have it repeated. But the teacher must not be led to devote a disproportionate amount of time to teaching these songs to children who are unable to sing them without considerable help.

V. Rhythmic Plays and Dramatizations

1. *Oats and Beans.* 2. *The Muffin Man.* 3. *The Farmer in the Dell.* 4. *The Seed Cycle.*

For the four traditional singing games the commonly observed directions are printed but these may be varied by the children, as they always have been in different times and regions.

VI. Listening Material

1. *Excerpts from Symphony No. VI (Pastoral),* Beethoven. A. *Allegro ma non troppo* (happy feelings awakened by arriving in the country); B1. *Allegro* (happy gathering of the country people); B2. *Allegro,* continued (a few peasants dance for the others); C. *Shepherd's Song* (happy and thankful feelings after a storm). 2. *Tambourin,* Mouret. 3. *Country Dance,* Dutch. 4. *Counting Out,* Rossman. 5. *Pastorale,* Mozart.

The eight instrumental pieces consist of four fragments from Beethoven's *Pastoral Symphony,* a Mozart *Pastorale* and a gay French dance, which are to be used at first for quiet listening and afterwards, if desired, for dramatization; and a Dutch folk dance and a counting-out tune, which are to be used for discriminating listening and discussion.

The best guide for appreciation of the Beethoven excerpts is found in his own description of the symphony as being "less an attempt to paint a picture than to recall the emotions awakened by a visit to the country." The teacher may give the descriptive words which Beethoven added to his music, but beyond that she may allow the music to speak for itself, without discussion. Suggestions for numbers three and four are printed with the music.

VII. Rhythm Band

1. *We Will Dance.*

This Austrian folk tune may be used for the rhythm band with the children devising ways for using the instruments which have been employed in other units or with the teacher adding a few other instruments and more formal suggestions for playing. It should be noted that *We Will Dance* consists of a single strain played twice, the first time softly and the second time a little louder. The children should probably play only on the first beat of each measure except in the last two when each note may be accentuated with the rhythmic instruments.

As usual, this single new composition may be supplemented by suitable pieces from other units.

III. Calls and Motives

1. Quack, Quack, Quack

2. The Cow

Quack, Quack, Quack.

Moo— Moo— Moo——

3. Dinner Time

4. Fol-de-rol-de-ri-do

Come chick chick, come and eat

Fol-de-rol-de-ri-do

5. Rice

6. My Gingerbread Man

I like cooked rice.

My Gin-ger-bread Man, is oh, so sweet.

7. Baby Duck

8. Counting Out

Ba-by duck knows how to float.

One, two, three, out goes he.

9. Shepherd's Song

Too-too-too-too-too *etc.*

IV. Songs

A. FOR CHILDREN TO SING

1. The Song of the Corn

David Stevens

Elizabeth Allen

1. The farm-er in the dell, He seeds the corn, Then
2. The farm-er on the hill, He husks the corn, The
3. The mil-ler in the mill, He grinds the corn, The

hoes, and hoes, and hoes the corn.
full ripe ears of gold-en corn.
mill goes round and grinds the corn.

1, 2   3

2. The Cow

F.A.R.
D.S.

Harriet Storrs

Moo - oo! Moo - oo!

Quietly

1. I help the farm - er at morn and night, And give sweet milk, to his
2. His wife makes but - ter on churn - ing day, And fresh cream cheese, from the
3. Such use - ful food, you can plain - ly see, You'd nev - er have, if it

great de - light.
curds and whey. Moo - oo! Moo - oo! Moo - oo!
weren't for me.

3. Little Red Calf

J. Lilian Vandevere

Gladys Pitcher

1. The lit-tle red calf is cute as can be. I vis-it the farm, and he stares at me. But when I am rea-dy to romp and play, He kicks his heels, and he scamp-ers a-way.

2. The lit-tle red calf is real-ly a clown. His heels will go up as his head comes down. I think he is talk-ing, I real-ly do, For he says "Maa!" when his moth-er says "Moo!"

4. Dinner Time

Czech Tune
Arranged by F. A. R.

Chick, chick, chick, Come and eat. Chick, chick, chick,

Come and eat. Chick, chick-ie, chick, Chick, chick-ie, chick, Come now and eat.

5. Quack! Quack! Quack!

S. B.

Stephene Blake

Moderato

1. Quack! Quack! Quack!
2. Quack! Quack! Quack!

Quack! Quack! Quack! See the lit - tle duck-lings go, Quack! Quack! Quack!
Quack! Quack! Quack! Wad-dling in a down-y row, Quack! Quack! Quack!

6. Fol-de-rol-de-ri-do

F.A.R.

Floy Adele Rossman

1. One lit-tle duck-ling swim-ming to and fro,
2. Two lit-tle duck-lings had no place to go,
3. Three lit-tle duck-lings swim-ming in a row,

Fol - de - rol - de, Fol - de - rol - de - ri - do, One lit - tle duck - ling
Fol - de - rol - de, Fol - de - rol - de - ri - do, Two lit - tle duck - lings
Fol - de - rol - de, Fol - de - rol - de - ri - do, Three lit - tle duck - lings

swim-ming to and fro, Heigh-ho, Fol-de-rol-de-ri - - do.
had no place to go, Heigh-ho, Fol-de-rol-de-ri - - do.
swim-ming in a row, Heigh-ho, Fol-de-rol-de-ri - - do.

7. Take Your Choice!

M. de H.

Mary de Haven
Accomp. by P.W.D.

Gaily

1. Milk in pud-ding, Milk in cus-tard, Milk in cot-tage cheese,____ And I en-joy the milk I get When eat-ing all these.____

2. Cream for but-ter, Cream for whip-ping, Strange as it may seem,____ But when they let me pick and choose, I'm tak-ing ice - - cream.____

8. The Milk Train

J. L. V.

J. L. V.
Accomp. by F. A. R.

1. Run-ning through the coun-try so ear-ly in the day.
2. Stop-ping at the sta-tions then up the grade and down.

Comes the nois-y milk train, To take the milk a - way.
Comes the nois-y milk train, To take the milk to town.

9. Rice

J. L. V.

J. Lilian Vandevere

I like cooked rice And I like rice cakes, I like puffed rice and I like rice flakes. But best of all I like rice pud-ding, The kind with rai-sins that moth - er makes.

10. Which?

Margery Armitage

Sarah Olds

FIRST CHILD

Bread is good to eat, Or-ange juice to

drink, Which do you like best? Choc-lit cake, I guess!

SECOND CHILD FIRST CHILD

11. My Gingerbread Man

A. E.

Ann Engels

Moderately slow

1. My Gin - ger - bread Man is
2. My Gin - ger - bread Man is

oh, so sweet, From the crown of his head, To his fun-ny brown feet.
thin and flat, He'd be more of a treat If he on-ly were fat.

12. Mister Farmer

J.L V

J. L.V.

1. The farm-er sows the
2. A-cross the fields in

corn and wheat. He plants the peas for us to eat. He
row on row His beans and beets and on-ions grow. He

sows the seeds, He hoes the weeds, So thank you, Mis-ter Farm-er.
works, you see, For you and me, So thank you, Mis-ter Farm-er.

1. A Chicken's Ways

Rowena Bennett

William Peters

2. A Smart Duck

Miriam Clark Potter

Peter W. Dykema

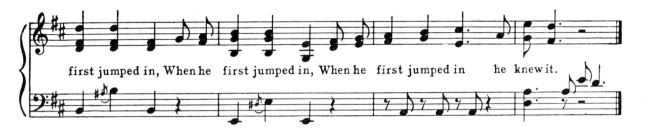

first jumped in, When he first jumped in, When he first jumped in he knew it.

3. The Barnyard Song

Kentucky Mountains Folk Song
Accomp. by H. W. Loomis

Allegretto moderato

1. I had a cat and the cat pleas'd me, I fed my cat by yon-der tree;
2. I had a hen and the hen pleas'd me, I fed my hen by yon-der tree;
3. I had a duck and the duck pleas'd me, I fed my duck by yon-der tree;
4. I had a goose and the goose pleas'd me, I fed my goose by yon-der tree;
5. I had a sheep and the sheep pleas'd me, I fed my sheep by yon-der tree;
6. I had a pig and the pig pleas'd me, I fed my pig by yon-der tree;
7. I had a cow and the cow pleas'd me, I fed my cow by yon-der tree;
8. I had a horse and the horse pleas'd me, I fed my horse by yon-der tree;
9. I had a dog and the dog pleas'd me, I fed my dog by yon-der tree;

mp

(Omit this measure in the first stanza)   Cat goes fid-dle-i-dee.

Hen goes chuck chuck, chuck chuck,   Cat goes fid-dle-i-dee.
Duck goes quack___ quack,___
Goose goes swish-y, swash-y,
Sheep goes baa___ baa,___
Pig goes griff-y, griff-y,
Cow goes moo___ moo,___
Horse goes neigh___ neigh,___
Dog goes bow, wow, bow, wow,

With each stanza repeat the enumerations of the preceding stanzas, always ending with "Cat goes fiddle-i-fee!"

mf *(Omit this measure in the first stanza)*

4. Farmyard Song

J.L.V.

Edvard Grieg, Op. 61, № 3

On the farm there's a roost-er, And he wakes us at five, There are geese there in the pas-ture, There are bees in the hive. The red cow is moo-ing, The pi-geons are coo-ing. "Quack! Quack!" goes the duck. The hen says "Cluck-cluck." Gen-tle sheep feed on

V. RHYTHMIC PLAYS AND DRAMATIZATIONS

1. Oats and Beans

Old Game

1. Oats and beans and bar-ley grow; Oats and beans and bar-ley grow; Do
2. First the farm-er sows his seed, Then he stands and takes his ease;—
3. Wait-ing for a part-ner, Wait-ing for a part-ner,—
4. Tra la la la la la la, Tra la la la la la la,—

you or I or an-y-one know How oats and beans and bar-ley grow?
Stamps his foot and claps his hand, And turns a-round to view the land.
Break the ring and choose one in, While all the oth-ers dance and sing.
Tra la la la la la la, Tra la la la la la la la.

Directions: Single circle, hands joined; one player in center as Farmer. Circle walks to left while sing-ing 1st stanza. 2nd stanza: Farmer goes through the action indicated by the words, the circle standing and doing the same. 3rd stanza: circle move to left while Farmer chooses a partner. On the last stanza cir-cle skips to left, while Farmer and partner skip to right. The partner so chosen becomes Farmer when the game is repeated.

2. The Muffin Man

Old Game

Briskly

1. Oh, do you know the muf-fin man, the muf-fin man, the
2. Oh, yes, I know the muf-fin man, the muf-fin man, the
3. Now two of us know the muf-fin man, the muf-fin man, the

muf-fin man, Oh, do you know the muf-fin man, That lives in Dru-ry Lane?
muf-fin man, Oh, yes, I know the muf-fin man, That lives in Dru-ry Lane.
muf-fin man, Now two of us know the muf-fin man, That lives in Dru-ry Lane.

Directions: Single circle, hands joined, one player in center. 1st verse: center player takes four skip-ping jumps forward and four backward in front of circle. The others jump in place, hands on hips, while they sing the second verse. Player in center and the one he is facing join hands and skip around inside the circle, as they sing third verse. The play is continued by repeating the action with the two players in cen-ter, the next time with four, etc. until all engaged are in the center. Sing the appropriate number with each repetition of third verse.

3. The Farmer in the Dell

Old Game

Not too fast

1. The farm-er in the dell,___ The farm-er in the dell,___
2. The farm-er takes the wife,___ The farm-er takes the wife,___
3. The wife___ takes the child,___ The wife___ takes the child,___

Heigh Ho! the Der-ry O! The farm-er in the dell.___
Heigh Ho! the Der-ry O! The farm-er takes the wife.___
Heigh Ho! the Der-ry O! The wife___ takes the child.___

4. The child takes the nurse, etc.
5. The nurse takes the dog, etc.
6. The dog takes the cat, etc.
7. The cat takes the rat, etc.
8. The rat takes the cheese, etc.
9. The cheese stands alone, etc.

Directions: Circle formation, with one in center for Farmer. Circle moves round to left. On the second verse Farmer chooses. Each verse the new-comer chooses another. Those chosen march within the circle in lockstep formation, the latest one chosen being at the front of the line. On the last verse all but the Cheese return to the circle, while everybody claps and the game is repeated with the Cheese acting as Farmer.

4. The Seed Cycle
(Music: The Farmer in the Dell)

The music is sung one or more times for each part of the action, according to the number of players and a-vailable space. The players are divided into groups of *Seeds; Wind; Rain;* the *Sun;* and one acts as *Farmer.* As all sing, the following, or an original pantomine may be enacted.

1. The farmer sows his seeds, etc.   *Seeds* curl up on the ground.

2. The wind begins to blow, etc.   *Wind* players run about waving arms.

3. The rain begins to fall, etc.   *Rain* players run about, fingers hanging down to indicate raindrops.

4. The sun begins to shine, etc.   *Sun* players walk slowly, arms up, palms forward

5. The seeds begin to grow, etc.   *Seed* players slowly rise, becoming Grain.

6 The farmer cuts his grain, etc.   Action as with scythe, *Grain* falls to ground.

7. The farmer binds his sheaves, etc.   He touches three at a time, who stand back to back.

8. And now the harvest's in, etc.   All skip around sheaves, hands joined.

VI. Listening Material

1. Excerpts from Symphony № VI (Pastorale)

Ludwig van Beethoven

A. Allegro ma non troppo: Happy feelings awakened by arriving in the country.

B1. Allegro: Happy gathering of country people.

B 2. Allegro, *(continued)*. A few peasants dance for the others.

C. Shepherd's Song: Happy and thankful feelings after a storm.

2. Tambourin

Mouret (1682-1739)
Arranged by F. A. R.

This composition may be used for discriminating listening by the children, with some such motivation as the following:

Although this music goes on and on with only one little tune, there are some places where the dancers could stop if they were too tired to continue until the very end. The music seems to say at these places

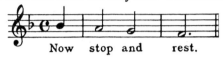

Now   stop   and   rest.

Can you tell how many such places there are?

3. Country Dance

Dutch Folk Dance
Arranged by F. A. R.

See the happy children playing, 'neath the shady maple tree.
Hear the leader gaily saying, "One, two, three, out goes he!"
Can you count the merry children, 'neath the shady maple tree?

One, two, three,   out goes he.

4. Counting Out

F.A.R.

Floy Adele Rossman

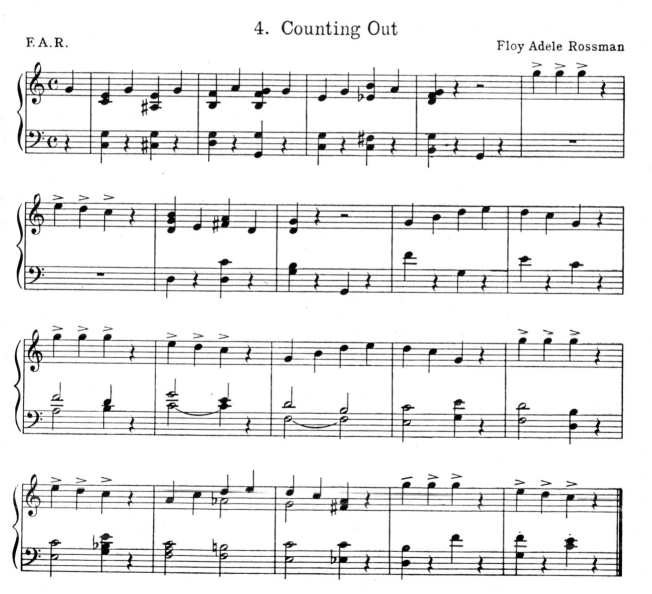

5. Pastorale

Wolfgang Mozart

D.C. al Fine

VII. RHYTHM BAND

1. We Will Dance

Austrian Folk Dance
Arranged by F. A. R.

Thanksgiving

I. Guiding Educational Principles

THANKSGIVING is one of the most difficult festal days to make significant for the young child. Although it is a natural celebration for the harvest of foods now stored for the winter, and although in America it commemorates the significant beginnings of our nation made by the Pilgrim Fathers, these are adult rather than childlike conceptions. The proximity of Christmas and the early preparations for celebrating that supreme children's holiday further complicate the making of an adequate Thanksgiving program.

Nevertheless, it is worthwhile to use this holiday as a time for considering the many matters for which we should be thankful, and without which our lives would be very different — the blessing of free religious worship, a rich and fruitful land, and the ties of home and friendship. Thanksgiving is a time to stop and think how fortunate we are to live in America, and, in a spirit of thankfulness, to consider what we can do for those not so fortunate as we.

II. Musical Applications

Since the purpose of our Thanksgiving celebration is primarily to affect the spiritual or emotional aspects of our life, to make us happy, thankful, and considerate, music is naturally called upon both to express and to stimulate the spirit of the day.

Two contrasting types of music are available; the quiet psalm of thanksgiving, and the romping, vigorous harvest song. Another note less familiar in the city, and no longer so common in the country, is that of the home gathering. But our children today still like the stories of the rural journeys which brought all the members of the widely scattered family together. Then we may also recall the music of the Indians who played such an important part in that first Thanksgiving Day. (See Unit Eight.)

III. Calls and Motives

1. *Pies for Sale.* 2. *The Turkey.* 3. *Hi! Ho! the Wagon.* 4. *Polly Put the Kettle On.* 5. *Thanksgiving Day.* 6. *There is a Happy Land.* 7. *O Rest in the Lord.*

These calls are drawn mainly from songs which appear in this unit. They lend themselves easily to tonal plays, both for rapid response, and for sustained singing. Some of them may be introduced independently, but most of them are so dependent for significance on the songs from which they are taken that the motive should be used only after the song has been heard.

IV. Songs

A. FOR CHILDREN TO SING. 1. *Pies for Sale.* 2. *The Turkey.* 3. *Hi! Ho! the Wagon.* 4. *Over the River.* 5. *Polly, Put the Kettle On.* 6. *Thank Thee, Lord.* 7. *Hymn of Joy.* 8. *For Thanksgiving.* 9. *Thanksgiving.* 10. *For the Beauty of the Earth.* 11. *Father, We Thank Thee.*

The first eight of these selections are complete little songs; the last three are portions of longer songs. All of them express in simple form some of the varied conceptions which appeal to young children at Thanksgiving time — fun, frolic, and food in the first five, and reverence and thankfulness in the last six. Several of these excerpts are taken from songs often sung in churches, and will thus enable the children to have at least a small part in adult services.

B. FOR TEACHER TO SING TO CHILDREN. 1. *Thanksgiving Day*, Bentley.

The lilt of this song may soon lead some of the children to join in with the teacher as she sings it. If the teacher desires she may sing to the children more of *O Rest in the Lord*, the alto solo from "*Elijah*," than is given in the Motives, possibly the first ten measures.

C. SUGGESTIONS FOR SINGERS. The sharply contrasted moods of both the motives and the songs in this unit offer excellent opportunities for leading the children to adapt their singing tones to the character of the music. Encourage them to show the differences in spirit by singing two or three songs such as *Pies for Sale, Hi! Ho! the Wagon*, and *Thank Thee, Lord!* with the same neutral syllable, lo or loo, while still indicating decided differences, such as lightness, strength, thankfulness, and quiet.

V. Rhythmic Play and Dramatization

A. SPECIAL INSTRUMENTAL MATERIAL. 1. *The Reaper's Song*, Schumann. Boys and girls may take turns in imitating the movements of the scythes as they cut the grain, making one big "swish," and its "back-swing" in each measure. Each group, walking and swinging slowly, works separately during the first four measures, which are repeated, then, reversing direction, does the same with the next four measures, with repetition. Finally, with one group going to the right and one to the left, all take part in the last four measures without repetition.

B. CREATIVE ACTIVITY. Although much of the preceding material requires original or creative activity by the children, they may be given further opportunities by constructing a Thanksgiving play which involves some of the songs and instrumental material presented in this unit. Topics or titles which may serve as centers are *Thanksgiving at Grandmother's; The First Pilgrim Thanksgiving; The Indian Harvest of the Corn.*

VI. Listening Material

1. *Hush, My Babe*, Rousseau. 2. *There Is a Happy Land*, S. S. Wesley. 3. *Come, Thou Fount of Every Blessing*, John Wyeth. 4. *The Spinning Wheel.*

Old Hundredth was one of the tunes brought to this country by the Pilgrims and constantly used by them. The first three tunes given are typical of the kind of music which was sung by children in the nineteenth century. They are presented as simple violin solos on Victor record 186226. Portions of the melodies are printed in this unit, but the complete tunes may be found in many hymnals, listed according to composers. The Spinning Song recalls an important occupation of the women and girls in the early days of our country.

III. CALLS AND MOTIVES

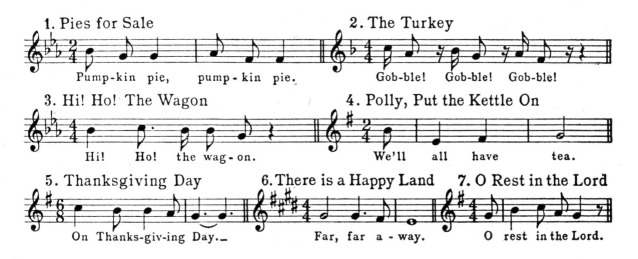

1. Pies for Sale

Pump-kin pie, pump-kin pie.

2. The Turkey

Gob-ble! Gob-ble! Gob-ble!

3. Hi! Ho! The Wagon

Hi! Ho! the wag-on.

4. Polly, Put the Kettle On

We'll all have tea.

5. Thanksgiving Day

On Thanks-giv-ing Day.

6. There is a Happy Land

Far, far a-way.

7. O Rest in the Lord

O rest in the Lord.

IV. SONGS

A. FOR CHILDREN TO SING

1. Pies for Sale

Anonymous

Old Tune
Arranged by P.W.D.

Pump-kin pie, pump-kin pie,

Come my la-dy, come and buy, Pump-kin pie, pump-kin pie,

Come and buy a pie. Then your chil-dren will not cry If they have a

pump-kin pie. Pump-kin pie, pump-kin pie, Come and buy a pie.

2. The Turkey

M.G.T.

Mona G. Tyer

The tur - key is a fun - ny bird, His head goes bob - ble, bob - ble, And all he knows is just one word, Gob-ble, gob-ble, gob-ble. Gob-ble, gob-ble, gob-ble.

3. Hi! Ho! the Wagon!

S. O.

Sarah Olds

Hi! Ho! the wag-on! Pump-kins piled so high!

Hi! Ho! Thanks-giv-ing! Gold-en pump-kin pie!

Hi! Ho! the wag-on! Tur-key comes to town.

Hi! Ho! Thanks-giv-ing! Tur-key's roast-ed brown.

4. Over the River

S. Maria Child

Old American Song

1. O - ver the riv - er, and thro' the wood, to grand - fa - ther's house we go.___ The horse knows the way to car - ry the sleigh Thro' white and drift - ed snow.___ O - ver the riv - er and thro' the wood, Oh how the wind does blow!___ It

2. O - ver the riv - er, and thro' the wood, and straight thro' the barn - yard gate.___ We seem to go ex - treme - ly slow, It is so hard to wait. O - ver the riv - er and thro' the wood, Now grand - moth - er's cap I spy!___ Hur-

stings the toes and bites the nose, As o - ver the ground we go.____
rah for the fun! Is the pud - ding done? Hur - rah for the pump - kin pie!____

5. Polly, Put the Kettle On

Traditional American Song
Accomp. by P. W. D.

Gaily

Pol - ly, put the ket - tle on,

Pol - ly, put the ket - tle on, Pol - ly, put the ket - tle on, We'll

all have tea. Su - key, take it off a - gain, Su - key, take it

off a - gain, Su - key, take it off a - gain, They've all gone a - way.

6. Thank Thee, Lord

Anon.

Theresa Armitage

Thank Thee for the world so sweet, Thank Thee for the food we eat.

Thank Thee for the birds that sing, Thank Thee, Lord, for ev - 'ry - thing.

7. Hymn of Joy

J. L. V.

Ludwig van Beethoven

God who gives us warm winds blow-ing, Star-ry nights and sun - ny days,

God who cares for all things grow-ing, Hear our hymn of grate - ful praise.

8. For Thanksgiving

J. L. V.

H. W. L.

1. Thank Him for fruit, thank Him for
2. He made them grow, all sum - mer

grain,   Thanks to the   Fa-ther, for the   sun   and the   rain.
long.   Thanks to the   Fa-ther, in   a   Thanks - giv - ing   song.

9. Thanksgiving

Stephen Fay   Johann Crüger

We   thank Thee, Lord, to - day,   For   good things with-out   num - ber.
For   guard-ing   us   in   play,   For   watch-ing   us   in   slum - ber.

10. For the Beauty of the Earth

F. S. Pierpont   Conrad Kocher

Lord   of   all, to   Thee   we raise   This   our hymn of · grate-ful praise.

11. Father, We Thank Thee!

                                             W. K. Bassford

Fa-ther, we thank Thee!   Fa-ther, we thank Thee!   Fa-ther, in heav-en, we thank thee!

1. Thanksgiving Day

A.E.B.

Alys E. Bentley

1. A bus - tle in the kitch - en, A smell of cakes and pies,___ Chil-dren run - ning ev - 'ry-where With bright and won - d'ring eyes.___
2. The tur - key's in the ov - en, The pump-kin's in the pie,___ Nuts and rai - sins in a dish With fruit are piled up high;___

Ap - ples in the ev - 'ning, Lots of noise and play,___
Sto - ries by the fire - light, When we're tired of play,___

All this fun at Grand - ma's, On Thanks-giv - ing Day,___

All this fun at Grand - ma's On Thanks-giv - ing Day.

V. RHYTHMIC PLAYS AND DRAMATIZATIONS

A. SPECIAL INSTRUMENTAL MATERIAL

1. Reaper's Song

Robert Schumann

VI. LISTENING MATERIAL

1. Hush, My Babe

Jean Jacques Rousseau (1712-1778)

2. There is a Happy Land

S. S. Wesley (1810-1876)

3. Come, Thou Fount of Every Blessing

John Wyeth (1792-1858)

4. The Spinning Wheel

Irish Folk Tune
Arranged by F. A. R.

Moderately fast

Repeat with treble octave higher

172

Character and Devotion

I. Guiding Educational Principles

ALTHOUGH the predominating note of childhood is, as it should be, one of happiness, this should not be interpreted to mean continuous jollity and laughter. Joy and satisfaction are found in quiet moments by children as well as by adults. Moreover, thinking is best promoted by reflection and contemplation. Periods of vigorous activity are rendered more enjoyable by intervals of rest and thought.

The school would be doing only part of its work if the children were merely carefree, flitting about like butterflies. Children enjoy examples of bravery and kindness and have satisfaction in trying to embody these characteristics in their own actions. An important function of the school is to make goodness attractive. The inclusion of a unit on character and devotion is therefore a logical and desirable procedure.

II. Musical Applications

Music is particularly suited to the development of fine character traits because it endows with a pleasant emotional tone everything that it touches. Even texts which by themselves might be dry or unattractive can be made pleasant and appealing by music. When the text is one which children already like for its own sake, the right kind of music not only adds to its charm but makes it much more easily remembered.

Pure instrumental music — that is to say, music without words or program — is potent with children as with adults in strengthening the appeal of any situation or idea with which it is appropriately associated. Religious instruction has always called upon music to reinforce its teachings: secular instruction is more and more using music to stabilize emotions and energize intellectual concepts.

III. Calls and Motives

1. *Taking Turns.* 2. *Brave.* 3. *Working Quietly.* 4. *Sing!* 5. *A Song for Happy Children.* 6. *Holy, Holy, Holy.* 7. *For Today.* 8. *O Worship the King.*

These themes are so nearly complete in themselves, that they can be repeated frequently without becoming uninteresting. They are also rich in character-building suggestions, and children should be encouraged to use them in school and at home.

IV. Songs

A. FOR CHILDREN TO SING AND HEAR THE TEACHER SING. 1. *A Song for Happy Children.* 2. *Keep Sunny.* 3. *Brave.* 4. *Running Errands.* 5. *Working Quietly.* 6. *Taking Turns.* 7. *Sing!* 8. *Little Milka.* 9. *When I Grow Up.* 10. *I Wonder Why.* 11. *On Time for School.* 12. *My Homeland.* 13. *Our Democracy.* 14. *For Today.* 15. *From the Twenty-Third Psalm.* 16. *God Sees.* 17. *His Care.* 18. *Come with Singing.* 19. *Praise.* 20. *Sing unto the Lord!*

The texts of the first songs stress general character traits; those of the last are concerned with devotional aspects.

V. Rhythmic Plays and Dramatizations

A. DRAMATIZING SONGS. Rhythmic movements or simple dramatizations may be used with several of the above songs, such as the first eight.

B. SPECIAL INSTRUMENTAL MATERIAL 1. *Dance of the Blessed Spirits* from "Orpheus", Gluck. In the mood of the lovely scene from Gluck's opera, the children may "step" sedately to this music, a slow step when the beat is un-divided (quarter notes), and two faster steps when the beat is divided into eighth notes.

VI. *Listening Material*

A. FOR QUIET LISTENING. 1. *Morning Prayer*, Gurlitt. 2. *The Bells*, Johnstone. 3. *At Church*, Tchaikovski. After the children have heard these pieces several times, a little dramatization or pantomime may be made of (1) Sunday morning prayer at home, (2) walking to church as the bells ring, and (3) sitting quietly in church for the service.

VII. *Rhythm Band*

1. *Marche Pontificale*, Gounod. For this impressive ceremonial march the children may decide how they would introduce, while still maintaining the religious character of the music, such instruments as the triangle, cymbals, gong, and possibly drum, usually played individually but possibly combined at the end.

III. CALLS AND MOTIVES

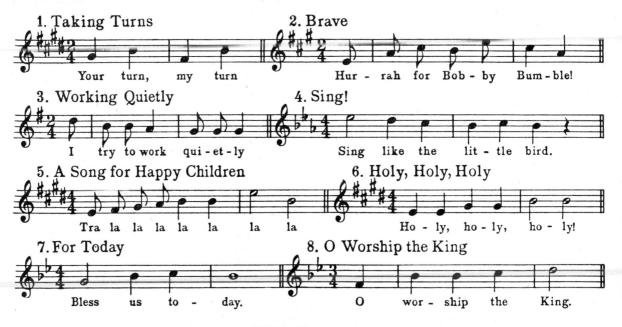

IV. SONGS

A. FOR CHILDREN TO SING AND HEAR THE TEACHER SING

1. A Song for Happy Children

Anon.

German Folk Tune
Accomp. by P. W. D.

174

way.   Tra la la la la la la la,   Hap-py all the day.

2. Keep Sunny

J. L. V.   Sarah Olds

Why should an - y - bod - y frown, Wear a mouth with

cor-ners down? Why should an - y bod - y pout? Wear your face the smile side out.

3. Brave

Emilie Poulsson   Eleanor Smith
                                                          (abridged)

Hur - rah for Bob - by Bum-ble! He nev - er minds a tum-ble, But

up he jumps and rubs his bumps, And does - n't ev - en grum-ble!

4. Running Errands

J. L.

Sarah Olds

Run-ning er-rands is lots of fun, When they're start-ed they soon are done. If you will try, you soon will see How ver-y help-ful you can be.

5. Working Quietly

J. L. V.

J. L. V.

I try to work qui-et-ly at what I have to do, So chil-dren all a - round me may do their work, too.

6. Taking Turns

J. L. V.

J. L. V.

1. Your turn, my turn, that's our
2. Your turn, John's turn, my turn

way; We like the plan of tak-ing turns, In all the games we play.
too; We like the plan of tak-ing turns, In ev-'ry thing we do.

7. Sing!

J.L.V.

J.L.V.
Accomp. by Charles Repper

1. Sing, like the ti - ny bird who ruf-fles ev -'ry
2. Sing, lit - tle chil-dren, sing, make mu-sic all to-

feath - er, With a heart full of hap - pi-ness to last him all day long.
geth - er. Fill your hearts full of hap - pi-ness by join-ing in a song.

8. Little Milka

T. A.

Russian Folk Song
Arranged by T. A.

Lit-tle blue eyed Mil - ka, Al-ways help-ing Moth - er, Hap-py in her home.
Bus-y lit - tle Mil - ka, Al-ways help-ing Fa - ther When the cat-tle roam.

177

9. When I Grow Up

Mary de Haven

Peter W. Dykema

Steadily, in march tempo

(Boys) When I grow up I'll run a train or fly the big-gest, fast-est plane. I mean to be, if I know how, as fine a man as Dad-dy.

(Girls) When I grow up I'll mend and cook and paint or sing or write a book. I mean to be, if I know how, as good and kind as Moth-er.

10. I Wonder Why

J. Lilian Vandevere

Charles Repper

Jon-a-than Jones went out with a frown, His

nose went up and his mouth went down. And then that eve-ning I

heard him say, "My, but peo-ple were cross to-day!"

Mil - li-cent Miggs went out with a smile, She gave out hap-pi-ness, all the while, And

then that eve-ning I heard her say, "Ev - 'ry-bod-y was kind to-day."

11. On Time for School

J. L. V.

Gladys Pitcher

1. John-ny is up in the morn - ing,
2. Ma - ry is up in the morn - ing,

Up and dressed by eight._____ He makes it a rule to start
Out of bed she'll climb._____ She goes on her way with-out

ear - ly for school, And so he nev - er is late._____
stop-ping to play, And so she's al - ways on time._____

12. My Homeland

E. A.

Elizabeth Allen

I am glad to be to-day safe in my Home-land.
I am proud to say to-day, (omit)_____ "This is my Home-land."

13. Our Democracy

D.S.

F.A.R.

De-moc-ra-cy shall live,— To keep our coun-try free. Where free-dom's ban-ner waves Is the land for you and me.

14. For Today

Anon.

Samuel Drake

Dear lov-ing Fa-ther, bless us to-day. Help us to work— well, Guard us at play.

15. From the Twenty-third Psalm

J. L. V.

The Lord is my shep-herd, the Lord is my

shep-herd, the Lord is my shep-herd, I shall not want.

16. God Sees

T. A.

Theresa Armitage

When I run a-bout all day,

When I kneel at night to pray, God sees, God sees.——

17. His Care

J. L. V.

J. Lilian Vandevere

1. At home, or in school, where-ev - er I may go, One thought I re - mem - ber, that is good to know. It rings in my heart, a hap-py lit - tle song, That God takes care of me, the whole day long.

2. At night in the dark, with-out a sin - gle fear, I sleep, and am rest - ing, for his love is near. I'm safe as can be, and this is al-ways true, For God takes care of me, the whole night through.

18. Come with Singing

From the Psalms   Gregorian

Come be - fore his pres - ence with sing - ing.

19. Praise

From the Psalms   Gregorian

Let ev - 'ry - thing that hath breath praise the Lord.

20. Sing Unto the Lord

From the Psalms   Susan Olds

Sing un-to the Lord! Sing un-to the Lord! Sing un-to the Lord a new song.

V. RHYTHMIC PLAYS AND DRAMATIZATIONS

B. SPECIAL INSTRUMENTAL MATERIAL

1. Dance of the Blessed Spirits
from "Orpheus"

Christoph von Gluck

Andante

p dolce

Fine

p

f

D.C. al Fine

VI. Listening Material

A. FOR QUIET LISTENING

1. Morning Prayer

Cornelius Gurlitt

2. The Bells

Arthur Edward Johnstone

3. At Church

Peter I Tchaikovski

VII. Rhythm Band

1. Marche Pontificale

Charles Gounod

Machinery and Tools

I Guiding Educational Principles

THE machines of today are a familiar factor in the child's life. They help to make his living convenient and comfortable, and he senses their importance as savers of time and energy in home and community.

For the younger children there is suggested a consideration of those machines most intimately connected with their experience. This will lay a groundwork for the further study of machinery as related to agriculture, industry, and transportation.

Children watch adults using tools, and they enjoy using small tools themselves. They see the plane, saw, and hammer being used by the carpenter, or on Daddy's work bench. The egg-beater, rolling-pin, and cookie-cutter make kitchen work a joy and an adventure, to boys as well as to girls.

II. Musical Applications

Many machines have some characteristic sound which will serve as the nucleus of a song. Such a song represents the child's early experience with things which "go." Where yesterday's child thrilled to fairy tales, today's child has daily contact with the magic of switches, electric plugs, and smoothly meshed wheels. Through the rhythm of these songs one can give the effect of that motion and energy which make machines vital to our world. Machines and tools have been chosen as the subjects of songs to show the beauty in controlled power, and man's mastery of that power for better living.

III. Calls and Motives

1. *The Vacuum Cleaner*. 2. *The Washer*. 3. *Trucks*. 4. *The Riveter*. 5. (a and b) *Mister Carpenter*. 6. *The Lawn-Mower*. 7. *The Oil-Burner*.

IV Songs

A. FOR CHILDREN TO SING. (a) Machines in the home; 1 *The Oil Burner*. 2. *The Refrigerator*. 3. *The Vacuum Cleaner*. 4. *The Washer*. 5. *The Toaster*. (b) Machines outside the home; 1. *The Two Trains*. 2. *The Merry-go-round*. 3. *Trucks*. 4. *The Steam Shovel*. 5. *The Riveter*. (c) Tools; 1. *Mister Carpenter*. 2. *Kitchen Tools*. 3. *Garden Tools*. 4. *The Lawn-Mower*.

B. FOR TEACHER TO SING TO CHILDREN. 1. *My Radio*.

C. SUGGESTIONS FOR SINGERS. The imitative sounds suggested in this unit will make valuable vocal plays. *The Vacuum Cleaner* uses a clear hum, *The Riveter* and *The Lawn-Mower* use the trilled "r" which calls for a free tongue, while *The Washer* takes deep breathing for the sustained "swish."

V. Rhythmic Plays and Dramatizations

Many tools and machines work with a definite rhythmic swing, and dramatizing various songs in this unit will provide suitable rhythmic activity.

In *The Vacuum Cleaner*, the children may move an imaginary cleaner back and forth in time to the hum. In *Mister Carpenter* they use the tools in free pantomime as they occur in the song. In *The Two Trains* they may form two lines, and represent the trains. In *Kitchen Tools* they pantomime the motions as suggested. In *The Lawn-Mower* a few children may move about the room pushing a mower. To the vigorous swing of *Country Gardens* the children may spade, rake and hoe. In spading they press the spade down with the left foot, lift the spade, and turn over the spadeful of earth.

In hoeing they keep time with motions which begin with a definite down stroke. The rake is drawn back and forth with long smooth strokes. In *The Merry-go-round* four children may make the machinery in the middle, four more grasping the outside hands of the inner four. The merry-go-round turns slowly, counter-clockwise, then faster, gradually stopping.

VI. Creative Music

The children may suggest tools and ma- chines which have not been mentioned in this unit, and they may express their ideas in simple sentences, such as, "The (naming the tool or machine) goes like this," or, "Hear the —— go," imitating the sound. In creative rhythms they may show the motion of using a certain tool, or the sound and movement of some machine, and let the others guess what has been represented. These simple sentences and rhythms may be developed by the children into very short but complete songs.

III. CALLS AND MOTIVES

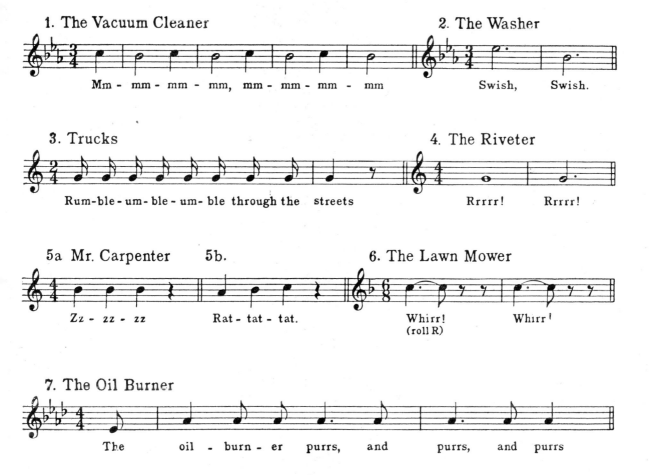

1. The Vacuum Cleaner

Mm - mm - mm - mm, mm - mm - mm - mm

2. The Washer

Swish,   Swish.

3. Trucks

Rum-ble-um-ble-um-ble through the streets

4. The Riveter

Rrrrr!   Rrrrr!

5a Mr. Carpenter   5b.

Zz - zz - zz   Rat - tat - tat.

6. The Lawn Mower

Whirr!   Whirr!
(roll R)

7. The Oil Burner

The   oil - burn - er   purrs,   and   purrs,   and   purrs

IV. Songs

MACHINES IN THE HOME

1. The Oil-Burner

J. Lilian Vandevere

Gladys Pitcher

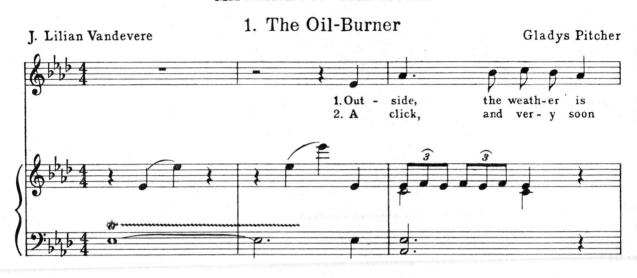

1. Out - side, the weath-er is
2. A click, and ver - y soon

damp and cold, The wind has brought a storm. But the
on it goes Though no one does a thing. And the

rit.   *a tempo*

oil-burn-er purrs, and purrs, and purrs, And the house is snug and warm.
oil-burn-er purrs, and purrs, and purrs, How I like to hear it sing.

2. The Refrigerator

J. Lilian Vandevere

Gladys Pitcher

1. The re-frig-er-a-tor's full of things to eat, It keeps them cold, it keeps them sweet; Eggs, cream, chops and steak, And ice-box cook-ies, to cut and bake.
2. There are or-ang-es of course, they're meant to squeeze, A bowl of soup, and good cream cheese; Milk, too, fresh to-day, And guess what's freez-ing, in one big tray.

3. The Vacuum Cleaner

J. L.V.

J. Lilian Vandevere

The vac-u-um clean-er hums, and hums, Mm-mm-mm-mm, mm-mm-mm-mm. It picks up all the dust and crumbs Mm-mm-mm-mm-mm-mm Un-der the chairs, and in be-tween, Sing-ing un-til the rugs are clean, The

vac-u-um clean-er hums and hums, Mm-mm-mm-mm-mm-mm.

4. The Washer

J. L.V.

J. Lilian Vandevere

1. Swish,　swish,　the wash-er is full,　Tow-els,　a-prons and socks.
2. Swish,　swish,　it wash-es the clothes,　Dad-dy's,　Moth-er's and mine.

A swish, swish, in foam-y white suds, Pa-ja-mas and ev-'ry-day frocks.
A swish, swish, and soon they are clean, And hang-ing to dry on the line.

5. The Toaster

J. Lilian Vandevere

Gladys Pitcher

1. For lunch we use a cas-se-role, For din-ner there's a roast-er; But when it comes to break-fast time, We use the toast-er.
2. You sim-ply turn the cur-rent on, A lit-tle while will heat it. Then out there pops a piece of toast, And you can eat it.

MACHINES OUTSIDE THE HOME

1. The Two Trains

J. L.

Jane Landon
Accomp. by R. S. Stoughton

1. The freight trains chug, chug, chug, chug, chug. Their puff, puff, puff is slow. But the pas-sen-ger trains go fly-ing through the coun-try, For they
2. The freight trains chug, chug, chug, chug, chug, With loads of heav-y freight. But the pas-sen-ger trains go fly-ing through the coun-try, For the

have to take the peo - ple Where the peo - ple want to go.
peo - ple have to hur - ry, And they nev - er want to wait.

2. The Merry-Go-Round

J. Lilian Vandevere

Gladys Pitcher

1. The mer - ry - go - round is a
2. The mer - ry - go - round is a

In the "tinkly" style of a merry-go-round

won - der - ful thing. We're buy - ing a tick - et, and tak - ing a ride. The
won - der - ful thing. The horse may be high but I clam - ber on top. He

last time ritard

an - i - mals frol - ic a - round in a ring, To mu - sic that's play - ing in - side.
gal - lops a - way with a dip and a swing, But soon he'll go slow - er and stop.

last time ritard

3. Trucks

J. Lilian Vandevere

Roy S. Stoughton

4. The Steam Shovel

Jane Landon   Gladys Pitcher

1. The steam shov-el's mouth is wide. Just see what it holds in - side! It gob-bles up clay, It gob-bles up sand, While dig-ging out a place for a house to stand.
2. It works ver - y hard each day, It bites and it bites a - way. The shov-el goes "Puff!" The shov-el goes "Roar!" Then stretch-es out its neck, as it looks for more.

5. The Riveters

J. L.

Jane Landon

*Rrrrr! Rrrrr! The big new build-ing ris-es high.

Rrrrr! Rrrrr! It al-most hits the sky. The

men are driv-ing riv-ets in, And oh, they make a

dread-ful din. Rrrrr! Rrrrrr! Just hear their ham-mers fly.

*Roll the "R"

1. Mister Carpenter

J.L.

Jane Landon

The car - pen - ter saws with a zz - zz - zz, And he planes till the boards are smooth and flat. Then he meas - ures with a rule, It's a ver - y hand - y tool, And he ham - mers and he ham - mers, with a rat - tat - tat.

J. L. V.

J. L. V.

1. It's fun in the
2. When moth-er makes

kitch-en, there's so much to do, I put on an a-pron so
cook-ies, she gives me some dough, I pat it down nice-ly, and

I may help, too. I like to turn the beat-er, I know how to hold it
roll it out, so. And then I cut some cook-ies, and bake them un-til they're

right, And I beat up the eggs till they're fluf-fy and light.
done. I can use all these tools, I think bak-ing is fun.

3. Garden Tools

J. Lilian Vandevere

Charles Repper

1. A shov-el, a rake, and a hoe, A shov-el, a rake, and a hoe, I like a set of gar-den tools, When things be-gin to grow.

2. A shov-el, a rake, and a hoe, A shov-el, a rake, and a hoe, Come on, get out your gar-den tools, And make your gar-den grow.

4. The Lawn-Mower

Helen Fitch

Stuart Bliss Hoppin

1. Whirr! (roll "r")   Whirr!   The lawn-mow-er's hum-ming a
2. Whirr!   Whirr!   A - round and a - round and a -

song.   It nib - bles the grass and leaves it neat.
round.   The lawn mow - er rolls and sings a song.

While it is pushed a - long.
Oh, such a bus - y (omit) - - - - - - - sound.

L.H.

1. My Radio

David Stevens

Gladys Pitcher

Not too fast

1. My
ra - di - o talks, and it tells me the news, And oft - en my ra - di - o

sounds from the sky, they are free to us all, A gift that so man - y may

asked my pa - pa to ex - plain it to me, I'd like to know just how it

sings,_____ And all I need do is to choose the right hour, And

share;_____ I just turn a knob and the mu - sic be - gins, Sweet

goes;_____ He says, "Well, per - haps I'll ex - plain it, some day,"— I

oh! the sweet mu - sic it brings._____ 2. These

songs that come straight from the air_____ 3. I've

won - der if he real - ly *(omit)* - - - - - - - - knows._____

V. RHYTHMIC PLAYS AND DRAMATIZATIONS

1. Country Gardens

Old English Morris Dance
Arr. by Gladys Pitcher

Pets and Toys

I. Guiding Educational Principles

LOSELY interwoven with the play element, which constantly appears in children with their pets, is the protective instinct. Dolls and dogs, alike, develop in the little girl and boy something akin to the mother and father feeling. Pets and toys, therefore, offer desirable possibilities for the growth of social attitudes. Health and safety for one's self frequently is an out-growth of the attempt to provide them for others. Neatness and order can easily be stimulated by the care of toys. Moreover, there is a reciprocal relation between the characteristics of living pets and their embodiment in art. Children who know pets are keen critics of songs which deal with them.

II. Musical Applications

Music can by suggestion reproduce and prolong many characteristics of pets and toys which appear only occasionally in the actual possessions or playmates of the child. The barking of the dog, the mewing of the cat, the rocking of the hobby-horse, the dancing of the doll, the jumping of Jack-in-the-Box — all these and many other movements can be idealized and repeated again and again in music. Pleasing musical settings may both lead the child to note whether they correspond to his playtime experiences and suggest to him new aspects of which he had not been aware while in the midst of his play. When appropriate music is used to accompany his play-activities they are regularized and enhanced.

III. Calls and Motives

1. *My Pets.* 2. *Come Kitty.* 3. (a and b) *Beware.* 4. *Naughty Peter Rabbit.* 5. *Pony Rides.* 6. *Lost Dolly.* 7. *Jack-in-the-Box.*

These song-themes should assist the children in creating calls or songs to their pets and playthings. Not all of them need words; humming or neutral syllables may be used.

IV. Songs

A. FOR CHILDREN TO SING. 1. *Come Kitty.* 2. *My Pets.* 3. *Beware.* 4. *Funny Clothes.* 5. *Naughty Peter Rabbit.* 6. *Good Morning! Little Pussy!* 7. *Pony Rides.* 8. *Funny Fish.* 9. *Lost Dolly.* 10. *My Train.* 11. *Macushla.* 12. *Teddy Bear.* 13. *Take Care of Them.*

These simple songs may be supplemented by similar ones drawn from preceding units, such as *What Did you see?*, *Rabbits*, and *The Brown Duck* in Unit One; *My Dog Teddy*, *A Funny Pincushion*, and *My Bunny* in Unit Two. Moreover, some of the children may create interesting songs about pets and toys.

B. FOR TEACHERS TO SING TO CHILDREN. 1. *The Stray Cat.* 2. *The Canary.*

V. Rhythmic Plays and Dramatizations

1. *Jack-in-the-Box.* 2. *The Pony Cart.* 3. *Wood-Pecker.* 4. *Copy-Cat.* 5. *Jack-Stones.* 6. *Dancing Doll.*

This material may be used in a variety of ways; as hand or finger movements while seated, as imitative action with an imaginary game of jack-stones, etc. Numbers 3 and 4 may also be used for quiet listening and the observation of the larger divisions of the music.

VI. Rhythm Band

1. *March of the Boys*, Bizet.

Rhythm instruments may be fitted in by the children both as a concert piece and for marching, with the players leading the procession of pets and toys. A record of Victor Herberts' March of the Toys may be used similarly.

III. Calls and Motives

1. My Pets
1. Bow - wow, bow - wow!
2. Mi - au, mi - au!

2. Come Kitty
Come Kitty, Kit - ty, Kit - ty!

3a. Beware
1. Soft - ly, soft - ly
2. Quick - ly, quick - ly

3b. Beware
1. Qui - et, qui - et
2. Scam - per, scam - per

4. Naughty Peter Rabbit
Naugh - ty Pe - ter Rab - bit

5. Pony Rides
1. Up the hill
2. Down the lane

6. Lost Dolly
1. Have you seen my dol - ly?
2. Have you seen my ?

7. Jack-in-the-Box
Good old Jack - in - the - Box.___

IV. Songs

A. FOR CHILDREN TO SING

1. Come Kitty

A.C.W.

Angela C. Wiechard

Come, Kit - ty, Kit - ty, Kit - ty, Come, Kit - ty, Kit - ty, Kit - ty, Where

can my Kit - ty be? Come, Kit - ty, Kit - ty, Kit - ty, Come,

Kit - ty, Kit - ty, Kit - ty, Are you hid - ing up there in the tree?

206

2. My Pets

H.F.

Sarah Olds

1. I've a pup-py dog that barks "Bow - wow! Bow -
2. I've a pus-sy cat that cries, "Mi - au! Mi -

wow!" When you throw a ball, he brings it, for I taught him— how.
au!" If you pat her head and stroke her, she'll start purr - ing— now.

3. Beware

T. A.

Theresa Armitage

1. Soft - ly, soft - ly, lit - tle mous - ie creep;
2. Quick- ly, quick- ly, lis - ten to ad - vice;

Qui - et, qui - et, Pus - sy is a - sleep.
Scam - per, scam - per, Pus - sy chas - es _ _ _ _ _ mice.

4. Funny Clothes

H.W. L.

H. W. Loomis

1. Mous - ie wears a vel - vet suit, soft and smooth and gray.
2. Bird - ie wears a feath - er suit, fish wear fins and scales.

Frog - gie wears a bath - ing suit, wears it ev - 'ry day.
Bun - nies all wear fur - ry suits, Trimmed with fluff - y tails.

5. Naughty Peter Rabbit

H.S.

Harriet Storrs

1. Naugh - ty Pe - ter Rab - bit!
2. Naugh - ty Pe - ter Rab - bit!

Oh, what shall I do? You nib - ble all the cab - bage heads, and all the car - rots too.
I know what I'll do, I'll plant some ten - der cab - bage heads, and they will be for you.

Naugh-ty Pe-ter Rab-bit, that's what I will do!

6. Good Morning, Little Pussy!

M. Beckman

Theresa Armitage

1. "Good morn-ing, lit-tle pus-sy, and how are you to-day?" "Good
2. "Come out, then, lit-tle pus-sy, and we will run and play." "I'm

morn-ing, mas-ter dog-gie, quite well, I'm glad to say."
sor-ry, mas-ter dog-gie, this is my bus-y day."

7. Pony Rides

Mary de Haven

French Song
Accomp. by P. W. D.

1. Up the hill, off to town, Ride your po-ny, fat and brown.
2. Down the lane, home at night, Ride your po-ny, small and white.
3. Through the woods, far a-way, Ride your po-ny, good and grey.
4. Trot-ting there, jog-ging back, Ride your po-ny, big and black.

209

8. Funny Fish

M. de H.

Mary de Haven
Accomp. by Gladys Pitcher

Gold-fish are such fun-ny fish, They nev-er make a sound. Still they're bright and sun-ny fish, A-swim--ming round and round.

9. Lost Dolly

A. C. W.

Angela C. Wiechard

"Have you seen my dol-ly?" "What did she wear?" "A lit-tle blue dress, With her soft gold-en hair."

10. My Train

J. Lilian Vandevere

Roy S. Stoughton

1. My train can run on a track.___ It goes a-round and back.___ Through a tun-nel, and past a bend, It goes for miles if I pre-tend. And then I stop it here,___ For I'm the en-gi-neer.___

2. Now see, I'm turn-ing a switch.___ I know which track is which.___ Watch the sig-nal, and see it drop. The sta-tion's here, the train will stop. I think a train is fun.___ I like to make it run.___

11. Macushla

T.A.

Irish Folk Tune
Arr. by T. A.

Go to sleep my lit - tle dol - ly, Lull - a - by, lull - a - by.

Puss and Ted - dy Bear are sleep - ing, Lull - a - by, lull - a - by.

12. Teddy Bear

J.L.

Jane Landon
Accomp. by Charles Repper

1. A ted - dy bear's al - ways round and fat, But his
2. A ted - dy bear's eyes are black and bright. He will

eyes are kind, and he nev - er minds that. He'll nev - er break, if you
wait all day, till you're sleep - y at night. Then you will find, when your

drop him on the rug. Ted-dy is the toy you can squeeze and hug.
last good-night is said, Ted-dy is the toy that you take to bed.

13. Take Care of Them

M. de H.

Mary de Haven
Accomp. by Gladys Pitcher

A pup-py or kit-ten will have to be fed, Give it wa-ter to drink and a nice warm bed.

Play with it gen-tly, and if you do, Your pet is sure to love you.

B. FOR TEACHER TO SING TO CHILDREN
1. The Stray Cat

H.W. L.

Harvey Worthington Loomis

A lit - tle or - phan pus - sy came creep - ing to our door. I let her have some bread and milk, and prom - ised her some more. I think that I'll a - dopt her, And keep her for my own, And

214

2. The Canary

tell her if she loves the birds to leave them all a - lone.

The yel-low ca-na-ry so soft-ly sings, Swee—

—swee— swee— The war - bling note is so

clear and high, Swee,— swee,— swee,— Pr - r - r - r - r.

V. RHYTHMIC PLAYS AND DRAMATIZATIONS

1. Jack-in-the-Box

S.B.

Stephene Blake

Good old Jack-in-the-Box,

Good old Jack-in-the-Box.

1. We give him a knock and
2. He's tied to a string and
3. He has a gay smile and

fas-ten the lock
moves on a spring.   Good old Jack-in-the Box.
nods all the while.

2. The Pony Cart

English version by
Getsie Samuel

Hindustani Folk Tune
Accomp. by Gladys Pitcher

Gal - lop quick - ly, gal - lop quick - ly, gal - lop quick - ly, broth - er horse.

1. We have still five miles of trav - 'ling,
2. Cru - el rob - bers may way - lay us.
3. Grain and grass be yours in plen - ty

And the shades of night are fall - ing.
What to do then? What to do then?
If we get home quick - ly, horse, So

Indian children perform this as an action song. During the chorus, hold reins and seem to urge horse on. During verse 1, show five fingers of left hand, and describe an arc with right hand to show nightfall. In verse 2 question neighbors anxiously. In verse 3 cup hands for "grain," pantomime a bundle for "grass," and spread hands for "plenty." During last chorus rise from seats and drive furiously.

From *Yours for a Song*. By permission of the compiler and publisher, Janet Tobitt.

3. Wood-Pecker

This rhythmic imitation game is especially good for a small-sized class. The teacher **may tap**, and the children, individually, will imitate. The patterns are given slowly and distinctly, especial care given to the problem of difficulty.

Tapping with a pencil is suggested, and with light taps.

Suggestions:

4. Copy-Cat

GAME OF THE CATBIRD

A child is chosen Catbird or Copy-Cat. He is sent from the room while several are selected to give various bird calls. The "Cat" must copy each call and give the name of the bird.

5. Jack-Stones

Arthur Edward Johnstone

Used by permission of Carl Fischer, Inc., owners of the copyright.

6. Dancing Doll

Eduard Poldini
abridged

VI. RHYTHM BAND

1. March of the Boys

Georges Bizet
from *Carmen*

UNIT FOURTEEN

Christmas

I. *Guiding Educational Principles*

ALTHOUGH Christmas is particularly significant because of its Christian interpretation, it is celebrated by almost the entire world regardless of creed or belief. The two universal ideas which it emphasizes are the reverence and joy associated with this festival, and the custom of exchanging gifts between family and friends. In the schools, December is the month for preparing and presenting the Christmas program. Normally peace and good-will are in the air and the spirit of brotherhood reigns. At no other time in the year is there such a strong feeling of co-operation; at no time is there a warmer friendship toward all with whom we come into contact. Educational efforts which are in tune with the season and are alive to its character-forming possibilities, take advantage of this happy spiritual period.

II. *Musical Applications*

Music, plenty of it, is inevitable at Christmas-time. When the heart is filled with happiness, song is a natural expression. The wonder and mystery of the oft-told story of the manger-birth is heightened and made more understandable when it is associated with beautiful music. The Christmas play needs rhythmic movement, guided and stimulated by music. No Christmas celebration is complete without appropriate music.

While there is fortunately an ample supply of Christmas music suitable for little children, much of the music they will hear is too difficult for them. Frequently, however, they can grasp little sections which in later years will help them to master the longer compositions.

III. *Calls and Motives*

1. *Jingle Bells.* 2. *A Cradle Carol.* 3. *Christmas Is Here.* 4. *Patapan.* 5. *Mary's Lullaby.* 6. *O Come, All ye Faithful.* 7. *Old English Round.* 8. *Joy to the World.* 9. *Silent Night.* 10. *Santa Claus Game* (of eight calls).

IV. *Songs*

A. FOR CHILDREN TO SING. 1. *Christmas Is Here.* 2. *Kolyada.* 3. *I Saw Three Ships.* 4. *When Santa Rides.* 5. *Christmas Packages.* 6. *Away in a Manger.* 7. *Christmas Secrets.* 8. *Making Presents.*

B. FOR TEACHER AND CHILDREN TO SING. 1. *Patapan.* 2. *A Cradle Carol.* 3. *Mary's Lullaby.* 4. *The Peppermint Cane.*

All of the songs in section A are simple enough for most young children to sing. Many children can also sing those in section B. But to assist the less advanced singers and to add interest for the entire group it is recommended that the B songs be sung antiphonally — the teacher singing the more difficult portions and the children answering with the simpler portions, these usually being repeated themes.

The children should learn all of these songs, not by direct teaching or drilling, but by hearing the teacher sing them once or twice a day throughout a period of two or three weeks. At first the children will merely listen. After a time a few of the brighter children will sing along with the teacher as she sings the complete song without stopping. In a few days most of the other children will join in the singing. Finally a light piano accompaniment may be used when everyone is singing.

If there is a portion of a song which the children sing incorrectly, the teacher may isolate that portion, and sing it over until it is clear in the children's minds, and they can sing it correctly. But there should be no formal and invariable teaching of songs phrase by phrase from beginning to end.

C. FOR TEACHER TO SING TO CHILDREN. For some groups, especially in preparation for programs given by older children which the entire school may attend, it may be desirable for the teacher to sing to the children songs of which only a part has been given in the Calls and Motives. Examples are numbers 6, 7, 8 and 9.

V. Rhythmic Plays and Dramatizations

1. *Jingle Bells.* 2. *The Wild Horseman.* 3. *March of the Three Kings.* 4. *Christmas Polka.*

Frequently the part which the little children are to play in the Christmas program will determine the rhythmic plays which they will use during the few weeks preceding it. These may be drawn from other units or from the four varied examples given here. These lend themselves to such different activities as Santa Claus driving his reindeer, a vigorous dance, a stately march of the Magi, and a dance about the Christmas tree. The first two pieces given under the next heading may also be used for vigorous expression. The Handel number (VI-3) might be used with a scene depicting the shepherds watching their flocks.

VI. Listening Material

1. *March* from the "Nutcracker Suite", Tchaikovski. 2. *Children's Christmas Piece,* Mendelssohn. 3. *He Shall Feed His Flock,* Handel.

As mentioned above these may be used for rhythmical expression, but they are also excellent for quiet listening. The first and third are easily available on phonograph records, from which longer portions may be played after the children are familiar with the excerpts.

VII. Rhythm Band

1. *March of the Toys,* Vandevere.

A considerable amount of material printed under other headings may be used for creative rhythm band expression along the lines indicated in preceding units. For instance, at the direction of the children, bells may be used with I Saw Three Ships, IV-A 3; rhythm sticks and drum with Kolyada, IV-A 2; drum and whistle with IV-B 1; bells and sticks with V-1; tambourine and drums with V-2; sticks, drums, cymbals, and bells with VI, 1 and 2.

We present also the *March of the Toys.* This may be played by the younger children either according to their own invention or according to the scoring given here, which would necessarily be taught by rote.

III. CALLS AND MOTIVES

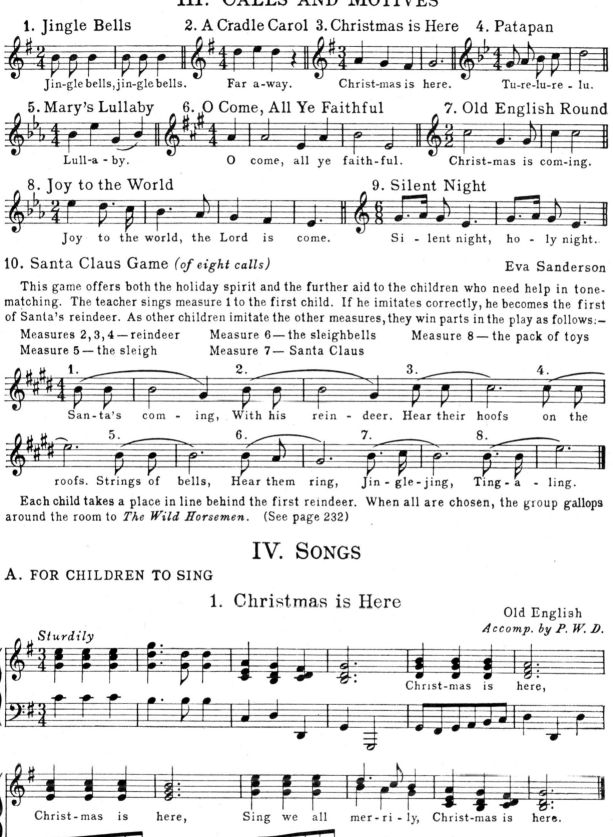

1. Jingle Bells

Jin-gle bells, jin-gle bells.

2. A Cradle Carol

Far a-way.

3. Christmas is Here

Christ-mas is here.

4. Patapan

Tu-re-lu-re - lu.

5. Mary's Lullaby

Lull-a - by.

6. O Come, All Ye Faithful

O come, all ye faith-ful.

7. Old English Round

Christ-mas is com-ing.

8. Joy to the World

Joy to the world, the Lord is come.

9. Silent Night

Si - lent night, ho - ly night..

10. Santa Claus Game *(of eight calls)*

Eva Sanderson

This game offers both the holiday spirit and the further aid to the children who need help in tone-matching. The teacher sings measure 1 to the first child. If he imitates correctly, he becomes the first of Santa's reindeer. As other children imitate the other measures, they win parts in the play as follows:—

Measures 2, 3, 4 — reindeer   Measure 6 — the sleighbells   Measure 8 — the pack of toys
Measure 5 — the sleigh   Measure 7 — Santa Claus

San-ta's com - ing, With his rein - deer. Hear their hoofs on the roofs. Strings of bells, Hear them ring, Jin-gle-jing, Ting - a - ling.

Each child takes a place in line behind the first reindeer. When all are chosen, the group gallops around the room to *The Wild Horsemen*. (See page 232)

IV. SONGS

A. FOR CHILDREN TO SING

1. Christmas is Here

Old English
Accomp. by P. W. D.

Sturdily

Christ-mas is here,

Christ-mas is here, Sing we all mer-ri-ly, Christ-mas is here.

2. Kolyada
(Yuletide)

D.S.

Ukranian Folk Tune

Kol-y-a-da, Kol-y-a-da, Christ-mas comes when morn-ing breaks.
Kol-y-a-da, Kol-y-a-da, Christ-mas pud-ding, Christ-mas cakes.

3. I Saw Three Ships

Old English Carol
Arranged by P. W. D.

1. I saw three ships come sail - ing in, sail - ing in, sail - ing in. I
2. Oh, they sailed in - to Beth - le - hem, Beth - le - hem, Beth - le - hem. Oh,
3. And all the bells on earth shall ring, earth shall ring, earth shall ring. And

saw three ships come sail - ing in, On Christ-mas Day, in the morn - ing.
they sailed in - to Beth - le - hem, On Christ-mas Day, in the morn - ing.
all the bells on earth shall ring, On Christ-mas Day, in the morn - ing.

4. When Santa Rides

A.C.W.

Angela C. Wiechard

1. When San - ta goes rid - ing a - round the world, The
2. They rock all their dol - lies the same as we, The

chil - dren o - ver the sea,___ They hang up their stock-ings, each
chil - dren o - ver the sea,___ So San - ta is good to us

224

5. Christmas Packages

J. L.

Jane Landon

boy and girl, And sing of the Christ - mas tree.
all you see, For that's what he likes to be.

1. See the Christ - mas
2. See the Christ - mas

pack - a - ges, With Christ - mas seals and bows!
pack - a - ges! I wrapped mine up to - day.

What there is tied up in them, Not an - y - bod - y knows.
Now I'll take them out with me, And give them all a - way.

6. Away in a Manger

Martin Luther

Old German Tune
Accomp. by P. W. D.

7. Christmas Secrets

J. Lilian Vandevere

Charles Repper

1. John-ny hid a bun-dle,
2. Some-thing in the clos-et,

Ma-ry hid a box,
Some-thing on a shelf,

I have hid-den some-thing
Some-thing tied with rib-bon,

In-
That

side a drawer that locks.
I have hid, my-self.

What the se-crets are

I can't say, But you'll find out on Christ-mas Day.

8. Making Presents

J.L.V.

J.L.V.
Accomp. by Gladys Pitcher

1. We're mak-ing a pre-sent for Moth-er,____
2. We're mak-ing a pre-sent for Fa-ther,____

We're mak-ing a pre-sent for Moth-er.____ We know what it will
We're mak-ing a pre-sent for Fa-ther.____ What it is we know

be, But you can't see. We're mak-ing a pre-sent for Moth-er.____
well, But we won't tell. We're mak-ing a pre-sent for Fa-ther.____

B. FOR TEACHER AND CHILDREN TO SING

1. Patapan

Translated from the French
by David Stevens

Old French Tune

Allegro

Wil-lie take your lit-tle drum, With his flute let Rob-in

228

come, Play as loud-ly as you can; Tu-re-lu-re-lu Pat-a-pat-a-pan. Make a

mu-sic bright and gay, Play a-way, It is Christ - mas Day.

2. A Cradle Carol

J. L. V.

Russian Folk Tune
Accomp. by Gladys Pitcher

Moderato

echo

1. Long a-go and far a-way, far a-way,
2. Ba-by Je-sus woke and smiled, woke and smiled,

mf

mp

echo

Fast a-sleep a ba-by lay, ba-by lay, O-ver-head a song filled the
Wise men came to see the child, see the child, Cra-dled in the hay He was

mp

qui-et night, O-ver-head a star gave a love-ly light.
ver-y small, Still He was a king, and the Lord of all.

229

3. Mary's Lullaby

Tr. by H.J.K. & J.W.C.

Tyrolean Carol
Accomp. by Joseph W. Clokey

Lull-a-by,__ lull-a-by.__ Lull-a-by my__ lit-tle__ one, Moth-er__ holds her child so ho-ly, Here a-mong the ox-en low-ly. Lull-a-by,__ lull-a-by.__ Lull-a-by__ my__ lit-tle one.

4. The Peppermint Cane

J. L.V.

J Lilian Vandevere

There once was a pep-per-mint cane; On a

230

V. RHYTHMIC PLAYS AND DRAMATIZATIONS

1. Jingle Bells

Old Song
Arranged by Samuel Lewis

Jin-gle bells,   jin-gle bells,   jin-gle all   the way,   Oh what fun it

is to ride in a   one-horse o - pen   sleigh.—   one-horse o - pen   sleigh.—

2. The Wild Horseman

Robert Schumann

3. March of the Three Kings

French Folk Tune
Used by Georges Bizet

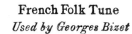

4. Christmas Polka

Swedish Folk Tune
Arranged by P. W. D.

VI. LISTENING MATERIAL

1. March

From the Nutcracker Suite

Peter I. Tchaikovski

2. Children's Christmas Piece

Felix Mendelssohn

3. He Shall Feed His Flock

George Frederick Handel
In *The Messiah*

VII. Rhythm Band

1. March of the Toys

J. L. V.

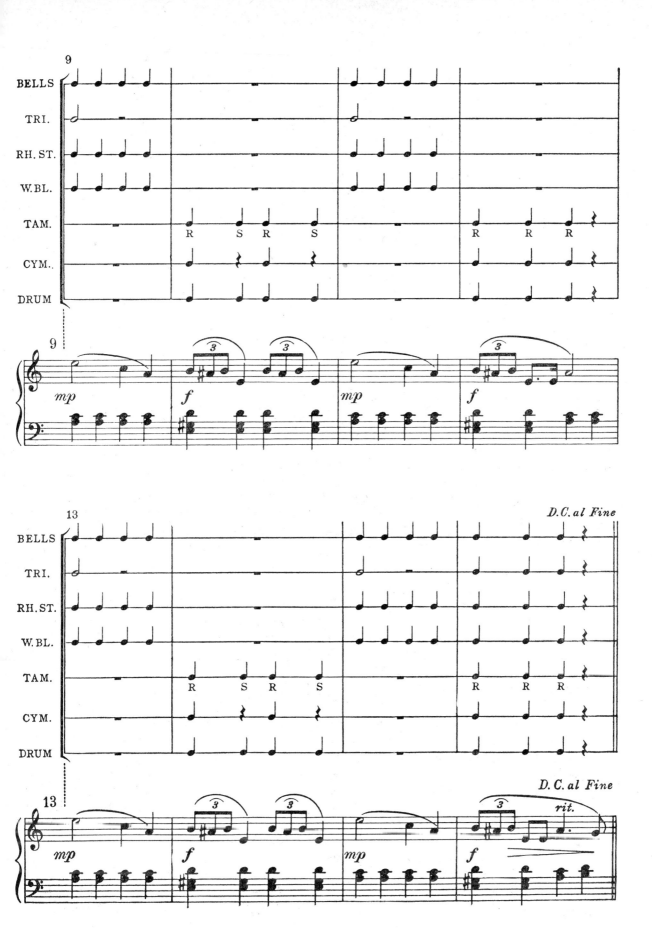

UNIT FIFTEEN

Winter

I. Guiding Educational Principles

LL life is dependent upon the adaptation of the living creature to his environment. It is the purpose of education to assist the learner to make necessary adaptations as economically and advantageously as possible. The more satisfactorily the child adapts himself to the changing seasons, the more effective his life will be.

Winter will be a pain or a pleasure to children largely according to the way they are guided to adapt themselves to it. Taking proper precautions, putting on and taking off adequate clothing, entering into winter sports, and, after a snowstorm, sensing the beauty and wonder of the great white world should be normal and joyful processes for most children.

II. Musical Applications

Because it can give the spirit and feeling-tone of experiences, music can be particularly helpful in bringing about appreciative attitudes toward the various aspects of winter. Just as a painting of a quiet snow-bound country-side, a colorful skating party, or a group of children building a snow fort may make us wish we were in the midst of similar experiences, so attractive songs may lead us to contemplate the beauty of the winter landscape, or to put aside the softer pleasures of indoors and brave the rigors of even severe winter weather.

III. Calls and Motives

1. *Wind Song.* 2. *Winter Nights.* 3. *Snowballs.* 4. *Fun in the Snow.* 5. *Drip, Icicles, Drip.* 6. *Look Out.* 7. *Zippers.* 8. *Broom Dance.*

IV. Songs

A. FOR CHILDREN TO SING. 1. *January.* 2. *Wind Song.* 3. *Dancing Snowflakes.* 4. *The Snowflakes.* 5. *Drifting Snow.* 6. *Fun in the Snow.* 7. *Frosty Snowman.* 8. *My Snowman.* 9. *Two Fine Sports.* 10. *Drip, Icicles, Drip!* 11. *Snowballs.*

B. FOR TEACHER TO SING TO CHILDREN. 1. *Winter Nights.* 2. *The Thermometer.* 3. *Zippers.*

V. Rhythmic Plays and Dramatizations

A. SINGING GAMES. 1. *Broom Dance.*

This old singing game may be related to the winter sport of curling, which resembles bowling and shuffleboard but is played with heavy disks or "stones." The sweeping of the ice by the "skip," to accelerate or retard the progress of the "stone," is an important feature. In the directions for the Broom Dance the lone player may be called the "skip."

B. SPECIAL INSTRUMENTAL MATERIAL. 1. *Skaters Waltz,* Waldteufel. 2. *Look Out (Throwing Snowballs),* Johnstone. The waltz may be used for pantomime skating by the children individually or in pairs. *Look Out* may be dramatized with throwing of snowballs. Allow the children to suggest movements, but encourage them to keep them rhythmical.

VI. Listening Material

1. *At Evening,* Schumann. 2. *The Rider's Story,* Schumann. 3. *Icicles Dripping,* Rossman. The early evenings of winter at home should bring music, reading, and story-telling for the young children. The two pieces by Schumann present the contemplative and the story-telling aspects.

VII. Rhythm Band

If the children desire they may, after discussion, add instruments to pieces in V-B and VI.

III. CALLS AND MOTIVES

1. Wind Song   **2. Winter Nights**

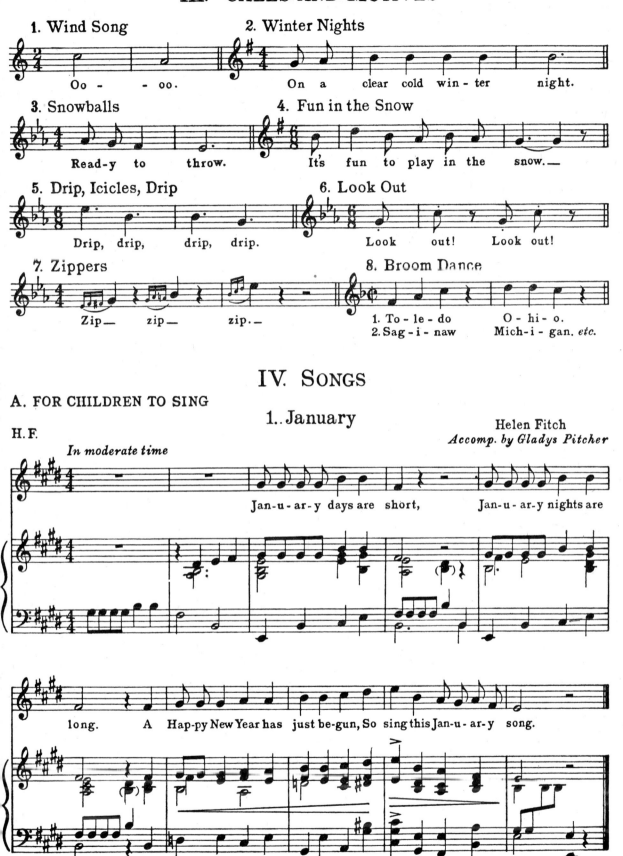

Oo - -oo.   On a clear cold win-ter night.

3. Snowballs   **4. Fun in the Snow**

Read-y to throw.   It's fun to play in the snow.—

5. Drip, Icicles, Drip   **6. Look Out**

Drip, drip, drip, drip.   Look out! Look out!

7. Zippers   **8. Broom Dance**

Zip— zip— zip.—   1. To - le - do   O - hi - o.
                2. Sag - i - naw   Mich - i - gan. *etc.*

IV. SONGS

A. FOR CHILDREN TO SING

1.. January

Helen Fitch
Accomp. by Gladys Pitcher

H. F.

In moderate time

Jan-u-ar-y days are short, Jan-u-ar-y nights are

long. A Hap-py New Year has just be-gun, So sing this Jan-u-ar-y song.

W. P.

2. Wind Song

William Peters

Boldly

Cold blows the wind,

Cold blows the wind. Oo - oo, Oo -

oo, Cold blows the wind, Cold blows the wind.

A.C.W.

3. Dancing Snowflakes

Angela C. Wiechard

Brightly

Snow-flakes danc - ing in the air, Whirl - ing, whirl - ing ev - 'ry - where.

4. The Snowflakes

By pupils of the Woodtick School,
R. F. D. 1, Wolcott, Waterbury, Conn.

Victor and Nancy Favara
Aged ten and eight

Nancy Favara

See the pret - ty snow - flakes, fall - ing from the sky.

rit.

On the hills and house - tops, soft and white they lie.

5. Drifting Snow

F.A.R

Floy Adele Rossman

Drift-ing snow, drift-ing snow. Soft and white, thru the night.
Morn-ing light, love-ly sight, Drift-ing snow, drift-ing snow.

6. Fun in the Snow

T.A.

Theresa Armitage

1. It's fun to play in the
2. It's fun to play in the

snow._____ Bun - dled warm as toast._____
snow._____ Take your sled and coast._____

7. Frosty Snowman

A.C.W.

Angela C. Wiechard

Frost-y snow-man. round and white, Likes to stay out - doors all night.

8. My Snowman

J. L. V.

French Folk Tune
Arranged by J. L. V.

1. Once I made a fun-ny
2. He was such a fun-ny

snow-man, He was ver-y round and fat. He was such a splen-did
snow-man, He was ver-y big and white But when I got up next

snow-man, And he wore my dad-dy's hat.
morn-ing, He had melt-ed out of sight.

0. Two Fine Sports

P. W. D.

Peter W. Dykema

Cheerily

Af-ter work-ing all day On a

big snow fort, Read-ing books be-side a fire Is an-oth-er fine sport.

10. Drip, Icicles, Drip!

Italian Folk Tune
Arranged by F. A. R.

F. A. R.

Rather slowly

Drip,   drip,   drip,   drip,

Drip,   i - ci - cles,   drip! _____   Drip,   i - ci - cles,   drip! _____

11. Snow Balls

Ann Engels

A. E.

The snow is soft for the snow ball fight. Roll it
We'll build a fort where we hide from sight.

round and read-y to throw.   throw.   Roll it round and hard, roll it

round and hard, Roll it round and read-y to throw.

1. Winter Nights

2. The Thermometer

mer-cu-ry falls when it's cold-er, And climbs when the weath-er grows hot.

3. Zippers

J. L. V.

J. Lilian Vandevere
Accomp. by Gladys Pitcher

1. Three lit-tle zip-pers on my snow suit,
2. I work the zip-pers on my snow suit,

Fas-ten up as snug as snug can be, It's a ver-y eas-y thing, as
Zip-pers real-ly do save time for me. I can fas-ten them my-self, with

you can see, Just zip!— zip!— zip!—
one, two, three, Just zip!— zip!— zip!—

V. RHYTHMIC PLAYS AND DRAMATIZATIONS

A. SINGING GAMES

Broom Dance
(Curling)

Old Game

One, two, three, four, five, six, sev'n, Where's my part-ner? nine, ten, 'lev'n,

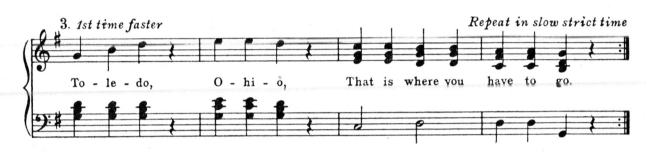

3. 1st time faster   *Repeat in slow strict time*

To - le - do,   O - hi - o,   That is where you   have to   go.

Players stand in two lines, facing, boys in one, girls in the other. An extra player goes up and down between the lines with a broom. 1. Players, singing, take four steps forward and back. 2. Repeat. 3. Each player takes a new partner, the extra partner dropping the broom and taking a partner if possible. On repeat partners dance together, the extra player with the broom, all dancing into place at the end of the music. Repeat as desired.

B. SPECIAL INSTRUMENTAL MATERIAL

1. Skaters' Waltz

E. Waldteufel
Arranged by Remington

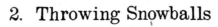

2. Throwing Snowballs
(Look Out!)

Arthur Edward Johnstone

VI. LISTENING MATERIAL

1. At Evening

Robert Schumann
Arranged

2. The Rider's Story

Robert Schumann

3. Icicles Dripping

Mother Goose and Other Tales

I. Guiding Educational Principles

THE story, especially when in verse or in repetitious prose, is a favorite means of entertaining and instructing children. Hence their fundamental conceptions of animal and human characteristics are usually based upon stories and rhymes heard in childhood. As information-quizzes frequently demonstrate, almost the only verses which many adults know today are of the Mother Goose stories.*

II. Musical Applications

Although a song text is more easily remembered if it is associated with a tune, it is nevertheless desirable for the children to learn these oft-quoted Mother Goose texts as verses before they meet them in songs. They can then better appreciate the lilt of the verses and the contribution the music makes to the words.

Many of the Mother Goose texts have been set to music that evidently was written for children who have long since left the nursery stage. We have therefore selected only the simpler settings for our young children to sing.

We have also included with musical settings two repetitive prose stories. These will at first be given entirely by the teacher. Later, if desired, some or all of the children may read the texts from the blackboard or chart or mimeographed sheets while the teacher plays the music.

III. Calls and Motives

1. *Mistress Mary.* 2. *Baa! Baa! Black Sheep.* 3. *See-Saw, Margery Daw.* 4. *Tame Animals.* 5. *Pussy-Cat.* 6. *Doodle-Doo.* 7. *Little

---

*Mother Goose is the American name for what the English call Nursery Rhymes. It is said that Elizabeth Foster was married to Isaac Goose, and for their children she gathered or made up many stories in verse form. Early in the eighteenth century she had published in Boston the first edition of *Songs for the Nursery, or Mother Goose's Melodies.*

Miss Muffet.* 8. *Humpty Dumpty* 9. *Johnny and the Three Goats* 10 *The Gingerbread Man.*

Since all of these calls are presented in keys of the songs from which they are taken, the teacher, if she desires, may sometimes allow a child to sing more than the motive. But, in general, time for singing entire songs should not be taken from the few minutes allotted for daily practice of all individuals on calls and motives.

IV. Songs

A. FOR CHILDREN TO SING. 1. *Baa! Baa! Black Sheep.* 2. *See-Saw, Margery Daw.* 3. *How Many Days?* 4. *Tame Animals.* 5. *There Was an Old Woman.* 6. *Pussy-Cat.* 7. *Hush-A-By-Baby.* 8. *Jack, Be Nimble.* 9. *Hey Diddle Diddle.* 10. *Doodle-Doo.* 11. *Little Bo-Peep.* 12. *Hickory Dickory Dock.*

B. FOR TEACHER TO SING TO CHILDREN. 1. *Little Miss Muffet.* 2. *Humpty Dumpty.* 3. *Ye Song of Sixpence.* 4. *Mistress Mary.*

No hard and fast line is to be drawn between songs listed under A and B. The teacher should feel free to interchange the classifications according to the interests and powers of the children.

Likewise, although directions for bodily movements are given for only one of the songs, IV-12, almost all of them lend themselves to rhythmic movements and dramatization. The children should be encouraged to originate these.

C. TALES WITH MUSIC. 1. *Johnny and the Three Goats.* 2. *The Gingerbread Man.*

When the children know these two story-songs, they may work them out as little music dramas, with action. In the Gingerbread Man, a group of children may be included in the threshers and mowers, thus giving many children a chance to take part. The role of the Gingerbread Man may be played by some especially capable child.

III. CALLS AND MOTIVES

1. Mistress Mary

Mis - tress Ma - ry, quite con - tra - ry.

2. Baa! Baa! Black Sheep

Baa! Baa! black sheep!

3. See-saw, Margery Daw

See - saw, Mar-ger-y Daw.

4. Tame Animals

1. Bow - wow - wow!
2. Meow - meow - meow!

5. Pussy-Cat

Pus - sy cat, pus - sy cat, where have you been?

6. Doodle-Doo

Doo - dle, doo - dle, doo —

7. Little Miss Muffet

Lit - tle Miss Muf - fet

8. Humpty Dumpty

Hump - ty Dump - ty

9. Johnny and the three Goats

I cry be-cause the boy cries.

10. The Ginger-bread Man

I'm the Gin-ger-bread Man.

IV. SONGS

A. FOR CHILDREN TO SING
1. Baa! Baa! Black Sheep

Mother Goose   Old English

Baa! Baa! black sheep, have you an-y wool? Yes, sir, yes, sir, three bags full;

One for my mas-ter, and one for my dame, And one for the lit-tle boy who lives down the lane.

2. See-saw, Margery Daw

Mother Goose   J. W. Elliott

See - saw, Mar-ger-y Daw, Jack shall have a new mas - ter,

He shall have but a pen-ny a day, Be-cause he won't work an-y fast-er.

3. How Many Days?

Old Rhyme

H. F.

How man-y days has my ba-by to play? Sat-ur-day, Sun-day, Mon - day,

Tues - day, Wednes-day, Thurs-day, Fri - day, Sat - ur-day, Sun-day, Mon - day.

4. Tame Animals

Mother Goose
Lively

Harvey Worthington Loomis
Accomp. by P. W. D.

1."Bow - wow - wow!"   "Whose   dog art
2."Meow,   meow,   meow!"   "Who   spoke just

thou?"   "Lit - tle Tom-my Tuck-er's dog,   Bow - wow - wow."
now"   "On - ly lit - tle pus-sy-cat,   Meow   meow   meow."

251

5. There Was an Old Woman

Mother Goose

William Peters

There was an old wo-man lived un-der a hill, And if she's not gone she lives there still

6. Pussy-Cat, Pussy-Cat

Mother Goose

J. W. Elliott

Pus-sy-cat, pus-sy-cat, where have you been? I've been to Lon-don to vis-it the Queen. Pus-sy-cat, pus-sy-cat,

what did you there? I fright-ened a lit-tle mouse un-der her chair.

7. Hush-a-by Baby

Mother Goose

Old English

Hush-a-by, ba - by, on the tree top, When the wind blows, the cra - dle will rock.

When the bough breaks, the cra - dle will fall, Down comes ba - by, cra-dle and all.

8. Jack be Nimble

Mother Goose

H. W. L

Jack be nim - ble, Jack be quick, Jack jump ov - er the can - dle-stick.

9. Hey, Diddle Diddle

Mother Goose

J. W. Elliott

Hey, did-dle did-dle, the cat and the fid-dle, The cow jumped o-ver the moon.___ The lit-tle dog laughed to see such sport, And the dish ran aft-er the spoon

10. Doodle-Doo

Old Rhyme

Floy Adele Rossman

Doo-dle-doo-dle doo, The prin-cess lost her shoe.___ Her high-ness hopped, The fid-dler stopped, Not know-ing what to do.___

11. Little Bo-Peep

Mother Goose

J. W. Elliott

Lit-tle Bo-Peep has lost her sheep, And can't tell where to find them.

Leave them a-lone, and they'll come home, Wag-ging their tails— be - hind them.

12. Hickory Dickory Dock

Mother Goose

Old Tune

Hick-o-ry dick-o-ry dock, *(tick-tock)* The mouse ran up the clock. *(tick-tock)* The

clock struck one, The mouse ran down, Hick-o-ry dick-o-ry dock. *(tick-tock)*

Directions: Double circle, partners facing. Hands down in front stiffly, representing pendulum. (1) Swing arms right, left, right; stamp twice on "tick-tock." (2) Change places with partner with short running steps, stamping again on "tick-tock." (3) On "the clock struck one," clap hands over head. (4) Run back to place; (5) Repeat swing and stamp. A second part may be done as follows: Join hands with partner, arms extended. Take three slides round circle and three stamps and repeat. On "the clock struck one," hold right elbow in left hand and extend right forefinger. At end, each turns in place, finishing with pendulum swing and stamps as at first.

1. Little Miss Muffet

Mother Goose

Sprightly

Helen C. Dykema

Lit-tle Miss Muf-fet sat on a tuf-fet, eat-ing her curds— and whey.— A- long came a spi-der and sat down be-side her, and fright-ened Miss Muf-fet a- way.—

2. Humpty Dumpty

Mother Goose

J. W. Elliott

Hump-ty Dump-ty sat on a wall, Hump-ty Dump-ty had a great fall All the king's hors-es, and all the king's men, Could-n't put Hump-ty Dump-ty to- geth- er a- gain.

256

3. Ye Song of Sixpence

Mother Goose

Old English

Sing a song of six - pence, a pock - et full of rye,
Four and twen-ty black birds baked in a pie. When the pie was o - pened the
birds be-gan to sing, Was-n't that a dain-ty dish to set be-fore the king.

4. Mistress Mary

Mother Goose

Helen C. Dykema

With a gentle swing

Mis - tress Ma - ry
quite con - tra - ry, How does your gar - den grow? ___ With coc - kle shells and
sil - ver bells And pret - ty maids all in a row. ___ With row. ___

C. TALES WITH MUSIC

1. The Gingerbread Man

Old Story adapted and set
by J. Lilian Vandevere

Once upon a time there lived a little old woman and a little old man. The little old woman made a gingerbread man. She rolled the dough out flat,

When the little old woman opened the oven door to see if he was done, The Gingerbread Man jumped out and ran away. The little old woman and the little old man ran after him, calling,

He called back,

And they could'nt catch him. Soon he met a cow who said (B. 2). But he called back, (D. 1).

On each verse, repeat all previous lines.

lit - tle old man
2. sil - ly old cow
3. fool-ish old horse,
4. barn full of thresh-ers. I can run a - way from you, I can.
(omit on verses 1, 2 & 3.)

The cow ran after him, but he called back, (C). And the cow could'nt catch him.
Soon he met a horse who said, (B-3). But he called back, (D-2).
The horse ran after him, but he called back, (C). And the horse could'nt catch him.
He came to a barn full of threshers who said, (B-4). But he called back, (D-3).
The threshers ran after him, but he called back, (C). And the threshers could'nt catch him.
He came to a field full of mowers who said, (B-4). But he called back, (D-4).
The mowers ran after him, but he called back, (C). And the mowers could'nt catch him.
Then he met a fox and said the same thing to him. But the fox said,

E

Well, well! Per - haps you would, But I'd not catch you if I could.

They came to a river, and the fox said,

Jump on my tail, and I'll take you a - cross. A little farther on he said,

Jump on my back, or you may fall off. A little farther on he said, Jump on my shoul-der, you

may get wet. A little farther on he said, The wa-ter is deep-er, jump on my nose.

And the Gingerbread Man did. The fox jumped out on shore and threw back his head.

The Gingerbread Man was half gone.
The Gingerbread Man was three-quarters gone.
The Gingerbread Man was *all* gone.

2. Johnny and the Three Goats

Old Story adapted and set
by J. Lilian Vandevere

Once there was a boy named Johnny. He had three goats. All day the goats ran about on the hill.
Every night Johnny went to drive them home. One evening the three goats ran off the road, jumped
over a fence, and landed in a turnip field. Johnny could not get them to come out again. He sat down
on the hillside and cried. Along came a hare.

A

1. (The Hare) Why do you cry, lit - tle boy?_____
2. (The Fox) Why do you cry, lit - tle hare?_____
3. (The Wolf) Why do you cry, lit - tle fox?_____
4. (The Bee) Why do you cry, lit - tle wolf?_____

B

(Johnny) cry be-cause I can't get the goats out of the tur-nip field.

C

1. (Hare)
2. (Fox)   I'll get those naugh-ty goats out of the tur - nip field._____
3. (Wolf)

The hare tried and tried, but the goats would not come. Then he sat down and cried, too. Along
came a fox. (verses A-2; D-1; C-2.)

The fox tried and tried and tried, but the goats would not come. Then he sat down and cried, too.
Along came a wolf. (verses A-3; D-2; C-3.)

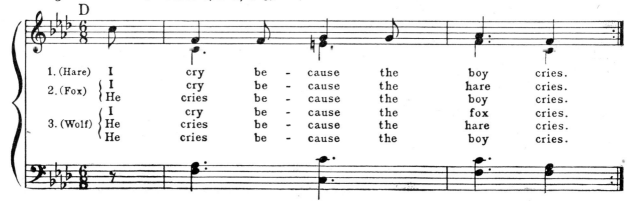

D

1. (Hare) I   cry   be - cause the boy cries.
2. (Fox)   I   cry   be - cause the hare cries.
           He   cries be - cause the boy cries.
3. (Wolf) I   cry   be - cause the fox cries.
           He   cries be - cause the hare cries.
           He   cries be - cause the boy cries.

He cries be-cause he can't get the goats out of the tur-nip field.

The wolf tried, and tried, and tried, and tried, but the goats would not come. Then he sat down and cried, too. Along came a bee. (verses A-4; D-3.)

(Bee) Why such a loud boo-hoo? Just see what I can do!

I'll get those naugh-ty goats out of the tur-nip field.—

(Boy)
(Hare)
(Fox)
(Wolf)

He thinks that he is strong-er than we— What a ri-dic-u-lous bee!—

(Bee) Bzz! Bzz! Bzz! Bzz! Bzz! Bzz! Bzz!—

And away ran the goats, every one!

Rhythmic Expression

I and II. Guiding Educational Principles and Musical Applications

ALL phases of rhythmic expression are treated at length in this unit, including free interpretation and the more informal use of rhythm instruments.

In a song the words float on the lilt of the melody. To the child, rhythm is the active part of the words. They come within the natural setting of the rhythm which they create. In this use of music, the mechanics of the metrical beat is not to be considered apart from the melody.

With continued singing and listening to music, the child's range of impressions and his analysis develop. With instrumental music, his emotional reaction to the rhythmic flow of the melody easily inspires a physical response. His muscular freedom in interpretation advances through his enjoyment of and reaction to musical experiences. Physical co-ordination is necessarily a slow growth so that many opportunities for musical expression are essential.

For the greatest educational development, all physical response to music at this age should come from within. The child's response is thus guided by his individual enjoyment of playing with the sounds of music. His body tells the story and his interpretation is a musical outlet for the ageless desire to do it himself.

Imposed interpretation greatly hinders all spontaneity. If the child is inspired by the music, he will respond to its rhythm. However poor his co-ordination may be, he will eventually be guided to some rhythmic regularity in his interpretation. If he is left free to grow in his interpretations, music becomes a part of his inner consciousness and is his own to interpret.

The rapidity of a child's progress in rhythmic expression is determined to a considerable degree by the ability of the teacher. She is also the guide in infusing the joys of listening as she herself listens and encourages the child to respond.

Group interpretation is developed through the use of such material as *The Clock*, mechanical toy or Indian songs, and through games, marches and rhythmic speech material. In these, the rhythmic response falls naturally into somewhat mechanical regularity. But even here, the inspiration comes from within, as each individual enjoys the responsibility of making a contribution to the rhythmic unison.

III. Calls and Motives

1. *My Piccolo.* 2. *The Kettle Drummer.* 3. *The Triangle.* 4. *The Tambourine.* 5. *Hot Cross Buns.*

IV. Songs

1. *The Kettledrummer.* 2. *My Piccolo.* 3. *The Tambourine.* 4. *The Triangle.*

With some of the songs found on other pages of the book a rhythmic instrument may easily be included:

Indian Music, Unit VIII (Use of drum and rattles.) *Ring for the King*, P. 78. (Triangles). *My Violin*, P. 8. (Rhythm sticks.) *Tick-Tock*, P. 20. (Rhythm sticks.) *The Fairy Piper*, P. 6. (Rhythm stick used as a flute.) *Bells of Osney*, P. 64. (Triangle.)

V. Rhythmic Plays and Dramatizations

A. DRAMATIZATIONS. 1. *My Dolly.* 2. *The Freight Engine.* 3. *Elephants.* 4. *Hot Cross Buns.* 5. *Butterflies.* 6. *Balloons.*

B. SPECIAL INSTRUMENTAL MATERIAL. 1. *Country Gardens.* 2. *Raindrops.* 3. *Molly on the Shore.* 4. *Bouree.*

VI. *Listening Material*

Since this unit is devoted entirely to rhythmic activity, no special material for listening, alone, has been provided.

VII. *Rhythm Band*

A. INFORMAL USE OF RHYTHMIC INSTRUMENTS.

Some of the music used for rhythmic interpretation may be supplemented by the use of children's rhythmic instruments. If the children are led to feel that each instrument may say something musically, it becomes an added means for rhythmic interpretation and not an end in the fundamental viewpoint of keeping time.

If the rhythm of a drum is always associated with the rhythmic movement of inspiring music, it is always a musical instrument to the child. It never becomes a mere noise maker. A drum inspires the strong beat of a march, the light taps of a running horse and the various dignified rhythms of Indian dances.

Rhythm sticks are the clock ticks or soft rain pats. If the children have watched the playing of a violinist, two rhythm sticks will easily become both violin and bow, to be held and played with musicianly care. Again, a rhythm stick may be a flute or piccolo as the length allows a free rhythmic fingering to the movement of the music.

Triangles as well as small bells "ring for the Queen" and other gay songs and dances. The use of either instrument strengthens responsibility for rhythmic regularity and precision. Triangles contribute advantageously to accompaniments of clock, bell and mechanical toy songs.

A concerted use of rhythmic instruments may follow the children's particular enjoyment of an instrumental number which has marked rhythm and simple dynamic changes. The children are led to notice the "loud and soft" passages and are encouraged in making sugges-

tions for the interpretive use of various instruments. Through experiments with different combinations and their appropriate use in various parts of the music, the children rapidly develop a discriminating analysis. They soon learn to frown upon too much noise and appreciate responsibility in helping to make a musical accompaniment to lovely music.

B. FORMAL USE OF INSTRUMENTS IN A RHYTHM BAND.

A more formal use of the instruments for a band may be advisable at times.

For example, in *Country Gardens*, the first and third beats are definitely strong throughout the number. The crisp energy of part A, makes this section at least a *mezzo forte* in tone. The use of the treble clef by the left hand, specifically determines part B as the soft section.

The teacher definitely selects the instruments to be used which in this case are drums, rhythm sticks, triangles and jingle sticks. The children holding the drums are asked to follow the loud beats of the music which are carefully accented by the musician at the piano. It is suggested that even in this formal use of instruments, the teacher refrain from counting the meter beat aloud. Let the children feel the accent from their recognition of its need in the marching rhythm. The melody of the folk tune is so simple, even with its dotted notes, that three year old children call it the "dum, dum-di-dum march". The pattern of the melody is easily followed by the tapping instruments.

Section A uses drums and rhythm sticks. In section B, triangles are substituted for the drums, and jingle sticks for the rhythm sticks. In A₂, all instruments are combined for the dramatic close. However, teachers are urged to guard against a too vigorous *fortissimo*.

As a band leader on parade is a familiar sight to most children, it is an easy matter to select an observant young leader who will conduct the march with precise down and up beats.

III. CALLS AND RHYTHMS

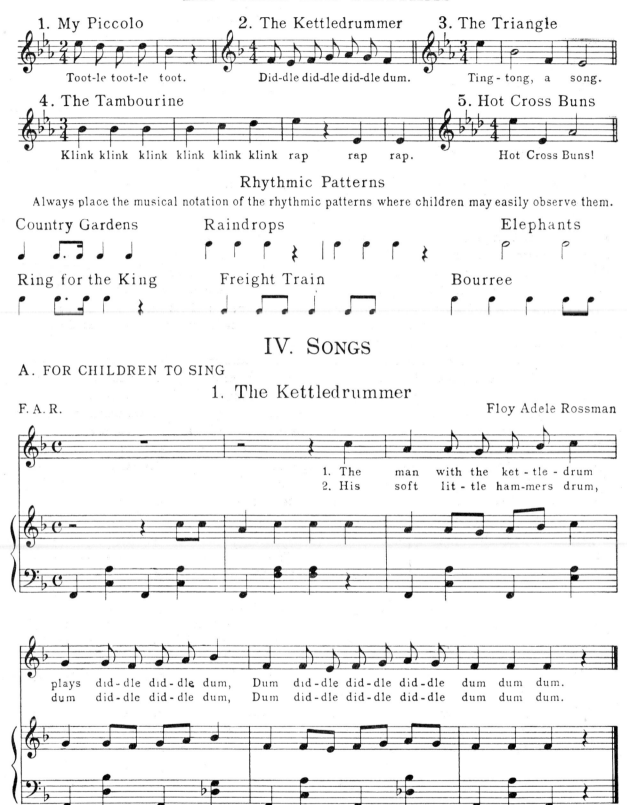

1. My Piccolo

Toot-le toot-le toot.

2. The Kettledrummer

Did-dle did-dle did-dle dum.

3. The Triangle

Ting - tong, a song.

4. The Tambourine

Klink klink klink klink klink klink rap rap rap.

5. Hot Cross Buns

Hot Cross Buns!

Rhythmic Patterns

Always place the musical notation of the rhythmic patterns where children may easily observe them.

Country Gardens   Raindrops   Elephants

Ring for the King   Freight Train   Bourree

IV. SONGS

A. FOR CHILDREN TO SING

1. The Kettledrummer

F. A. R.   Floy Adele Rossman

1. The man with the ket - tle - drum
2. His soft lit - tle ham-mers drum,

plays did - dle did - dle dum, Dum did - dle did - dle did - dle dum dum dum.
dum did - dle did - dle dum, Dum did - dle did - dle did - dle dum dum dum.

This song gives opportunity for alternating use of the hands.   Two pencils with erasers make most acceptable hammers.   Encourage suppleness with the wrists rather than the arms.

2. My Piccolo

H.S.

Harriet Storrs

My pic - co - lo sings high, my
Too - toot - le - toot - le - too, too-

pic - co - lo sings high, It plays a ver - y sau - cy tune, my pic - co - lo sings high.
toot - le - toot - le - too, It plays a ver - y sau - cy tune, too - toot - le - toot - le - too.

D. S.

3. The Tambourine

S.B.

Stephene Blake

Hear the gay tam - bour - ine tap - ping a tune,

Klink, klink, klink, rap, Klink, klink, klink, rap, Feet gai - ly dance to the

light tap - ping tune, Klink, klink, klink, klink, klink, klink, rap, rap, rap.

4. The Triangle

Floy Adele Rossman

1. The tri - an - gle's sing-ing a song, ting-
ring - a - ting, ting - a - ting tong, ting-

tong   The tri - an - gle's sing-ing a song.   2. A -
tong.   The tri - an - gle's sing-ing a _ _ _ _ _ _ _ _ _ _ _ song.

(repeat treble octave higher)

The striker of the triangle is to be held within the bounds of the instrument, and the first beat of the rhythm is naturally accented by the down stroke. With frequent use of the triangle, a preparation is made for the leadership of three-part rhythm.

V. RHYTHMIC PLAYS AND DRAMATIZATIONS

A. DRAMATIZATIONS

1. My Dolly

Floy Adele Rossman

Mechanically

1. I have a lit-tle dol-ly and she walks,   And she
2. I have a lit-tle dol-ly and she talks, *(ma-ma)* And she

walks,   And she walks,   She's a   cun-ning lit-tle dol-ly when she
talks, *(ma - ma)* And she talks, *(ma - ma)* She's a   cun-ning lit-tle dol-ly when she

walks,   She's a   ver-y cun-ning dol-ly, when she walks.
talks, *(ma - ma)* She's a   ver-y cun-ning dol-ly, when she talks. *(ma - ma)*

Head ornaments of a crepe paper band and bow will aid the dramatization of each dolly.   Leave the children to their individual interpretation of mechanical arm and head movements.

Throughout the second verse,   wherever the dolly speaks, the accompanist gives a prolonged retard.   There must be ample time for each doll to bend over and whine out the word.

2. The Freight Engine

Floy Adele Rossman

(Choo-choo-ca-choo, choo-ca-choo, choo-ca-choo, *etc.*)

Children feel the rhythm of the song through the use of the words, "Choo, Choo-ca-choo, Choo-ca-choo." The sound of the steam is imitated through a brisk rubbing of the palms of the hands.

In the dramatization, the engine may be built with a cow-catcher,—a child leaning over with hands out-stretched,—a smokestack waves its smoke through the use of small hands lifted high. The wheels are the large drivers or are small according to the response to the rhythm. An engineer may be added to blow the whistle or ring the bell.   The entire group participates by "riding in the caboose". Their feet lightly scuff the even beat, and the hands keep the rhythm of the escaping steam.

3. Elephants

Ponderously

Floy Adele Rossman

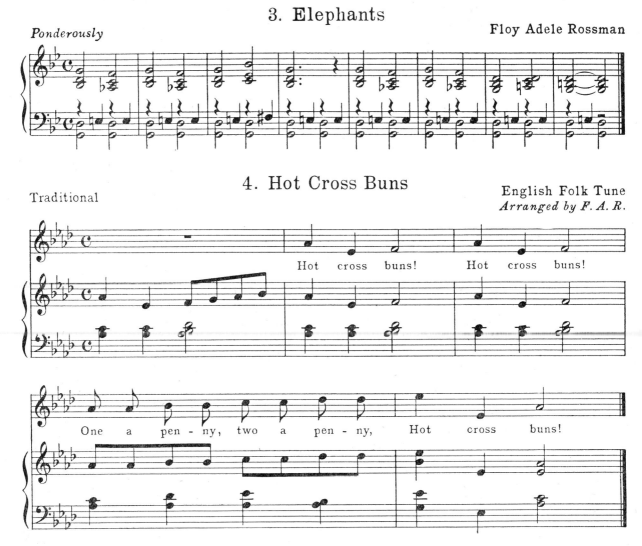

4. Hot Cross Buns

Traditional

English Folk Tune
Arranged by F. A. R.

Hot cross buns! Hot cross buns!

One a pen-ny, two a pen-ny, Hot cross buns!

Tell the story of the Hot Cross Bun Man who used to carry his basket of hot cross buns all carefully covered. He walked slowly along the street, anxiously looking to the right and left. With a hand
to the side of his mouth, he called his wares, hoping that the busy housewife would buy.

The dramatization may be made by several children at the same time.

5. Butterflies

Butterflies without a care
Float upon the summer air;
Lazily they pause to say,
"Lovely flower, Oh, good day;"
Then they lightly skim away.

F.A.R.

Concone, Op. 37, No 2

Allegro

Butterflies is presented for free rhythmic interpretation. The accompanist gives a sufficiently long pause through the quarter and half notes of each phrase, so that the butterflies may have time for a whispered conversation as they hover over each blossom.

6. Balloons

Floy Adele Rossman

To toss a balloon, and catch it in rhythmic response, depends not only upon physical co-ordination but upon judgement in timing the distance to which the balloon is flung as well as its weight. It is suggested that the music be interpreted at first with imaginary balloons. If real experience is desirable, use rather large balloons and let the children at first hardly loose them from the finger tips as the arms are flung upward. The interpretation of this number is valuable for the development of co-ordination in rhythmic response.

B. SPECIAL INSTRUMENTAL MATERIAL

1. Country Gardens

English Folk Tune
Arranged by F. A. R.

A fuller version of this number may be found in Unit Twelve.

2. Rain Drops

Rhythmic motive

F. A. R.

Ann Engels

The words of *Rain Drops* are to be spoken as the rhythm of the words is "patted" on the desk with a light click of the fingernails.

3. Molly on the Shore

Cork Reel
Arranged by F. A. R.

This is presented for light "tip-toe" running. An accompaniment of a triangle and kettledrum tapping may be used.

4. Bourree

Old French Tune
Arranged by F. A. R.

Repeat softly 8va

Fun and Fancy

I. Guiding Educational Principles

ALL normal young children are fond of fun and fancy, if these words are considered in their simple meanings. But the terms take on such different and complicated forms during advancing years that we tend to assign to children intricate conceptions which are only rarely present. Fun for them is almost anything that is pleasant, frolicsome or nonsensical. Fancy is little more than the association of ordinary things or actions which usually are not related. The surprise element looms large in both, but in the former it is usually external, and in the latter, internal.

The circus clown with his exaggerations is probably the nearest approach to what all young children would call funny; the incongruities of the idea of the dish running away with the spoon and the cow jumping over the moon form a fair average of the fancies of childhood.

The friendly teacher will always be sympathetic to the wishes and expressions of the child and will allow these to develop naturally unless they tend to harm the child or the group.

II. Musical Applications

Fun and fancy in music usually are embodied in the text or story associated with it. So strong is this literary appeal that most children have to be helped to find these qualities in the music itself. In adequate settings the fun or fancy of the text is expressed by the music associated with it, and the children's attention should be directed to this association.

Instrumental music, both the quiet type and that used for vigorous physical expression, is excellent for developing fun and fancy which is not dependent on exact expression in words. Sharp contrasts in the music — high and low, fast and slow, smooth and uneven, sweet and harsh, close-moving and leaping, ordinary and unusual — these are the elements which stimulate laughter, and the quaint speculations of young children. But sustained imagination is hardly to be expected of little children.

Moreover, even the simpler enjoyments of fun and fancy in instrumental music are gained by most children less from their giving careful attention to the music than from catching the atmosphere which the wise teacher, having selected suitable material, reflects in her reaction to it.

III. Calls and Motives

1. *Playing in the Band.* 2. *Bubbles.* 3. *Six Little Mice.* 4. *Just Suppose.* 5. *John and I.* 6. *How They Go.* 7. *Blowing Bubbles.* 8. *Just Fun.* 9. *The Musical Goblin.* 10. *A Silly Song.*

IV. Songs

A. FOR CHILDREN TO SING. 1. *The Musical Goblin.* 2. *A Silly Song.* 3. *Just Suppose.* 4. *John and I.* 5. *How They Go.* 6. *Blowing Bubbles.* 7. *Playing Frog.* 8. *Just Fun.* 9. *Brownie's Rest.* 10. *Mister Turtle.* 11. *Come and See!*

B. FOR TEACHER TO SING TO CHILDREN. 1. *Pussy Willow.* 2. *A Joke.*

V. Rhythmic Plays and Dramatizations

A. SONGS. 1. *Six Little Mice.* 2. *Bubbles.*

B. SPECIAL INSTRUMENTAL MATERIAL. 1. *Song of the Shoes.* 2. *The Crested Hen.* 3. *Jo an' de Banjo,* Kepper.

VI. Listening Material

1. *The Balloon,* Johnstone. 2. *Humoresque,* Tchaikovski. 3. *Dance of the Clowns,* Mendelssohn.

VII. Rhythm Band

1. *Playing in the Band.*

III. Calls and Motives

1. Playing in the Band

Hi!   Ho!   Hey!

2. Bubbles

Bub - bles,   Bub - bles.

3. Six Little Mice

1. I'm a lit - tle mouse.
2. We are lit - tle mice

4. Just Suppose

What would ev - ry - bod - y think?

5. John and I

1. John does, I do.
2. I do, John does.

6. How They Go

Toads go hip-pi-ty hop—

7. Blowing Bubbles

You can have such fun.

8. Just Fun

1. I baked a flash of light ning.
2. I ate a ray of sun -shine.

9. The Musical Goblin

Too, too, too, too, too, too, too.

10. A Silly Song

1. A - tid - dle tad - dle too - dle tum, A - did - dle dad - dle doo - dle dum.
2. A - lid - dle lad - dle loo - dle lum, A - fid - dle fad - dle foo - dle fum.

IV. Songs

A. FOR CHILDREN TO SING

1. The Musical Goblin

Danish Folk Song
Arranged by T.A.

T.A.

1. There once was a gob-lin who played on a horn: Too, too, too, too, too, too,
2. He played the horn soft - ly, and then made it loud: Too, too, too, too, too, too,

too.   He played it at night and he played it at morn: Too, too, too, too, too, too, too.
too.   And aft - er he played it he stood up and bowed: Too, too, too, too, too, too, too.

273

2. A Silly Song

Jane Landon

French Folk Tune
Accomp. by P. W D.

1. Tom-my Tuck-er learned a song And he sang it all day
2. Then Jack Horn-er made it worse, For he wrote an-oth-er

long. Such a sil-ly lit-tle rhyme, But he sang it all the
verse. Then he sang it to the birds, And they chuck-led at the

time. A - tid - dle tad-dle too-dle tum, A - did-dle dad-dle doo-dle dum.
words. A - lid - dle lad-dle loo-dle lum, A - fid - dle fad-dle foo-dle fum.

3. Just Suppose

S. O.

Sarah Olds
Accomp. by Gladys Pitcher

If grass were white and snow were green, 'T would

be a sight we nev-er have seen. If ros-es were black and ink were pink, Oh

rit. *a tempo*

what would ev-'ry-bod-y think?

4. John and I

J.L.V.

J.L.V.
Accomp. by Gladys Pitcher

1. Who likes to hear the pi-geons coo? John does,
2. Who goes to pick the pink-est rose? I go,

I do. Who likes to hear the bees go "buzz!" I do, John does.
John goes. Who runs to play in all the snow? John goes, I go.

5. How They Go

Creole Tune
Accomp. by H. W. Loomis

Fish go swim-ming roost-ers walk, Toads go hip-pi-ty hop.

Leaves go danc-ing, then they fly. Peach-es hang till they drop.

6. Blowing Bubbles

French Folk Tune
Accomp. by Roy S. Stoughton

You can have such fun When you start to blow a
That is how it's done, And it's not a bit of

7. Playing Frog

Margery Armitage

Elizabeth Allen

8. Just Fun

J.L.V.

Harvey Worthington Loomis
Accomp. by J.L.V.

1. I baked a flash of light-ning, I
2. I ate a ray of sun-shine, I

fried a sil-ver moon, I stirred them all to-geth-er With a pea-nut-but-ter spoon.
drank a glass of smoke, I jumped in-side a bub-ble, But the song is all a joke.

D. S.

9. Brownie's Rest

Frederic Manley

Gladys Pitcher

1. When a tir-ed lit-tle Brown-ie Longs to
2. In a lil-y bell he lays him; Then the

go to rest, Soon he finds a pret-ty, down-y, Daint-y, coz-y nest.
wind of night Sings a croon-y song and sways him Till the east grows bright.

10. Mister Turtle

F.A.R.

Floy Adele Rossman

Mis-ter tur-tle plods a-long, plods a-

278

long, plods a - long, Has no voice to sing a song, And
might not sing if he had one, ___ He might not sing if he had one.

11. Come and See!

Jane Landon

Dutch Folk Tune
Accomp by Roy S. Stoughton

1.See! See! See! Three birds are in a
2.Look! Look! Look! Three ducks are in the

tree! One can chirp and one can sing, One is just a
brook! One is white and one is brown, One is swim-ming

ti - ny thing. See! See! See! Three birds are in a tree! ___
up-side down. Look! Look! Look! Three ducks are in the brook! ___

D. S.

1. Pussy Willow

H.W. L.

Harvey Worthington Loomis

1. Pus - sy Wil - low wears her mit - tens, Like the cun - ning lit - tle kit - tens, But I
2. Pus - sy Wil - low, tell me wheth - er You ob - ject to chil - ly weath - er; If you

don't be - lieve she ev - er could purr. Oh, you pret - ty Pus - sy Wil - low, Won't you
do I think you real - ly would mew. If you'll come with me and moth - er, I will

let me make a pil - low Of your fluf - fy, muf - fy pus - sy - cat fur.
let you see your broth - er. He's a pearl - y grey An - gor - a, like you.

2. A Joke

J. Lilian Vandevere

Gladys Pitcher

"There's a hole in my coat," I

told my moth - er, And she sighed and said, "You're a care - less lit - tle soul! I must

mend it to-day, for you have no oth- er," Then I laughed and said "It's a but-ton-hole!"

V. RHYTHMIC PLAYS AND DRAMATIZATIONS

A. SONGS

1. Six Little Mice*

David Stevens
and Edwin Wright
(adapted)

Roy S. Stoughton

1. I'm a lit-tle mouse,
2. We are lit-tle mice,

I'm a lit-tle mouse, I'm a lit-tle mous-ie, too___ I'm a lit-tle mouse,
Tim-id lit-tle mice, Don't let cats come near us, please!___ We are lit-tle mice,

I'm a lit-tle mouse, I'm a lit-tle mous-ie, too.___
Hun-gry lit-tle mice, We would like a piece of cheese.___

*From the operetta "A Slip of the Slipper." C. C. Birchard & Co., publishers.

2. Bubbles

T. A.

Harriet Storrs

I am blow - ing bub-bles, bub-bles, bub-bles. bub-bles

Through the verse, the right hand is lifted to the mouth to blow the bubble, which is then tossed away. Through the piano part, the full pantomine of dipping the pipe into the bubble dish, blowing the bubble and watching it float away is desirable.

B. SPECIAL INSTRUMENTAL MATERIAL

1. Song of the Wooden Shoes

Dutch Folk Tune
Arranged by F.A.R.

2. The Crested Hen

Danish Folk Tune
Arranged by **F. A. R.**

3. Jo an' de Banjo

Charles Repper

VI. LISTENING MATERIAL

1. The Balloon

Arthur Edward Johnstone

Used by permission of Carl Fischer, Inc., owners of the copyright.

2. Humoresque

Peter I. Tchaikovski
Arranged by F. A. R.

3. Dance of the Clowns

Felix Mendelssohn
In *Midsummer Night's Dream*

VII. Rhythm Band

1. Playing in the Band

J. L. V.

French Folk Tune
Arranged by P. W. D.

1. I play on my tam-bour-ine,
2. I play on my lit-tle drum,
3. I play on my wood-block too,
4. The tri-an-gle's tone is clear,
5. The cym-bals are loud and strong,

Let me show you how I play. Rap and make it jin-gle,
Let me show you how I play. Rub-a-dub I'm beat-ing,
Let me show you how I play. First I light-ly tap-it,
Let me show you how I play. Strike to set it ring-ing,
Let me show you how I play. Just like this I clash them,

Shake and make it tin-gle.
Then I keep re-peat-ing.
Then I loud-ly rap it. Hi! Ho! Hey! Such an eas-y thing to play.
Strike to set it sing-ing.
Just like this I crash them.

Spring

I. Guiding Educational Principles

FOR the adult, spring signifies the rebirth of life in nature but for the child it means primarily the regaining of freedom of movement. Buds and flowers, birds and animals are of less importance to him than the casting aside of his heavy winter clothing and the opening of doors and windows. Only a little guidance is needed to aid the child to get pleasure from watching the new world of growing things about him. His sense of color and beauty are easily stimulated. The care of pets and flowers may awaken interests that will help him to understand many otherwise perplexing questions in later years.

II. Musical Applications

With sensitive composers, the music inspired by Spring is predominantly hopeful, happy, and even gay. Mingled with it is frequently a note of contemplation that may be more appealing than the merry strain.

Both of these moods appeal to young children, the former spontaneously — for skipping is a natural expression of happiness —, the latter after a little guidance or contact with an appreciative teacher — for wonder is natural to all unspoiled children.

Spring songs frequently have refrains of neutral syllables or nonsense lines as if to indicate that, when joy abounds, words with definite meanings are unnecessary. Much of the instrumental music lends itself to gay rhythmic movements and dancing. Music of spring should bring joy and the free expression thereof.

III. Calls and Motives

1. *Dear Little Buttercup.* 2. *May Day.* 3. *Lavender's Blue.* 4. *Pussy Willow.* 5. *I Saw a Star.* 6. *One Misty, Moisty Morning.* 7. *Spring Bells.* 8. *Dandelion.* 9. *The Garden.* 10. Theme from *First Symphony*, Schumann.

IV. Songs

A. FOR CHILDREN TO SING. 1. *Dear Little Buttercup.* 2. *Good Gardening.* 3. *A June Tune.* 4. *The Hurdy Gurdy Man.* 5. *Lavender's Blue.* 6. *Jumping Ropes.* 7. *Pussy Willow.* 8. *I Saw a Star.* 9. *The Shepherd Maiden.*

B. FOR ANTIPHONAL SINGING, TEACHER AND CHILDREN. 1. *One Misty, Moisty Morning.* 2. *Spring Bells.* 3. *Dandelion.*

The songs in section B may be sung by the teacher alone, or responsively with the pupils. As far as possible only such subdivisions should be made as will heighten the significance or dramatic value. Repetitions of a musical phrase are effective when sung by different voices, and a fine way of making clear the distinction between a narrative portion and an exact quotation is to have them sung by different persons. The poorer singers should be asked to sing only the portions given in the Calls and Motives.

V. Rhythmic Plays and Dramatizations

A. SINGING GAMES. 1. *The Garden.* 2. *Apple Blossoms.* 3. *May Baskets.*

B. SPECIAL INSTRUMENTAL MATERIAL. 1. *A Little Dance*, Mozart.

VI. Listening Material

1. *Morning Mood*, Grieg. 2. *All About April*, Vandevere. 3. *Rondo-Caprice*, Beethoven. 4. *Spring Song*, Henselt

VII. Rhythm Band

Percussion instruments may be used effectively with IV-A 2, 5 and 6; IV-B 1, 2, 3; V-A 2, 3; V-B 1; and VI 1, 2, 3.

III. Calls and Motives

1. Dear Little Buttercup

1. How are you?
2. Ver - y well.

Lav - en - der's green.

2. May Day

May Day, May Day

3. Lavender's Blue

Lav - en - der's blue,

4. Pussy Willow

Mi - au! Mi - au! Mi - au!

5. I Saw a Star

1. I saw a star
2. High up a - bove

6. One Misty, Moisty Morning

Oh how do you do?

7. Spring Bells

Ring, ding - a - ding, ding - a - ding, dong bell!

8. Dandelion

Fluff - i - ty, fluff - i - ty, fluff, fluff, fluff

9. The Garden

1. This is how we dig the ground.
2. This is how we rake the ground.
   etc.

10. Theme from 1st Symphony, Schumann

(Hark! sounds of spring are ev - 'ry - where)

IV. Songs

A. FOR CHILDREN TO SING

1. Dear Little Buttercup

Words and Music by
William **Reid**
six years old

Dear lit - tle but - ter - cup, How do you do? Oh, I am ver - y well, How are you?

2. Good Gardening

H. F.

Sarah Olds

1. Plant the seeds,   Weed and
2. If you work,   Some fine

hoe,   Wa - ter the gar - den, And watch it grow.
day   You will have po - sies To give a - way.

3. A June Tune

J.L.V.

Samuel Drake
Accomp. by Gladys Pitcher

Lazily

1. Sing Heigh, Ho! for a day in
2. Sing Heigh, Ho! for a place to

spring, Sing Heigh, Ho! for a chance to swing. Sing Ho,
dig, Sing Heigh, Ho! for a pool that's big. Sing Ho,

Hum! for a place to lie, Watch-ing the clouds go by. ____
Hum! what a la - zy tune, All a - bout days in June. ____

4. The Hurdy-Gurdy Man

T. A.

Italian Folk Tune
Arranged by T. A.

The hur - dy-gur - dy comes, ____ I hear it play, ____ The

288

hur - dy - gur - dy man _____ is on the way. Tra la la

la la la la la la la, Tra la la la la la la la la la, Tra la la

la la la la la la la, Tra la la la la la la la lay.

Traditional

5. Lavender's Blue

Old English Song

Gaily

1. Lav - en - der's blue, dil - ly dil - ly, Lav - en - der's
2. Call up your men, dil - ly dil - ly, Set them to
3. Some to make hay, dil - ly dil - ly, Some to cut

green. When I am king, dil - ly dil - ly, you shall be queen.
work, Some to the plough, dil - ly dil - ly, some to the cart.
corn, While you and I, dil - ly dil - ly, keep our - selves warm.

289

6. Jumping Rope

Samuel Drake
Accomp. by Jane Landon

J. L.

1. There's a queer lit-tle rap-rap- rap-ping, There's a
2. Lit-tle shoes make a rap-rap- rap-ping, Lit-tle

queer lit-tle slap, slap, slap. There's a queer lit-tle tap-tap-
ropes make a slap, slap, slap. Lit-tle feet make a tap-tap-

tap-ping, Oh, it's fun, jump-ing rope in spring.
tap-ping, And they jump to the song we sing.

7. Pussy Willow

Stephene Blake

S. B.

Allegro

Mi - au!__ Mi-au!__ Mi-

290

8. I Saw a Star

H.C. D.

Helen C. Dykema

9. The Shepherd Maiden

J.L.V.

French Folk Tune
Accomp. by P. W. D.

1. A maid-en made a cheese, Oh! Sing fol - de-rol, and a fol - de-ray, A cheese to charm and please, Oh! And set the thing a - way, fa-lay, Up - on a sum - mer day.
2. She said to Puss who saw it, Sing fol - de-rol, and a fol - de-ree, "You must not pat or paw it, For you can sure - ly see, fa-lee, How naugh-ty that would be."
3. Puss blinked her green eyes bright - ly, Sing fol - de-rol, and a fol - de-red, And an-swered her po - lite - ly. "I will not pat or paw," she said, "I'll use my tongue in - stead."

B. FOR ANTIPHONAL SINGING, TEACHER AND CHILDREN
1. One Misty, Moisty Morning

Mother Goose

Peter W. Dykema

Gaily, but not too fast

One mist - y, moist - y morn - ing, when cloud - y was the weath-er, I chanced to meet an old man

cloth-ed all in leath-er. Then he be-gan to com-pli-ment, and

I be-gan to grin; Oh, how do you do, and how do you do, and

how do you do a-gain. Oh, how do you do, and how do you do, and

how do you do a-gain.

2. Spring Bells

F.A.R.

Floy Adele Rossman

Gaily and lightly

Ring, ding-a-ding, ding-a - ding-dong bells!

Spring has come, so the warm wind tells. Ring, ding - a - ding, ding - a -

ding-dong bells! Spring has come, ring the gay May bells.

Ring, ding-a - ding-dong bells!

3. Dandelion

Charlton C. Edholm

William Peters

Dan-de-li-on, fun-ny fel-low.

Yes, you are a fun-ny fel-low, Yes-ter-day all gold-en yel-low!
Gold's all gone but does it mat-ter? You've a thou-sand seeds to scat-ter.

Now you are of diff-'rent stuff, Just a down-y ball of fluff.
They'll be fly-ing soon e-nough, Watch them fly when I go puff.

Fluff-i-ty, fluff-i-ty, fluff, fluff, fluff.
Puff-i-ty, puff-i-ty, puff, puff, puff.

V. RHYTHMIC PLAYS AND DRAMATIZATIONS

A. SINGING GAMES

1. The Garden

French Singing Game

1. This is how we dig the ground, In our gar-den, in our gar-den. This is how we dig the ground, In our lit-tle gar-den bed.

2. Rake the ground. 3. Sow the seed. 4. Hoe the weeds. 5. Pick the corn.

2. Apple Blossoms

A.E.

Ann Engels

Moderato

Ap-ple blos-soms fall like snow, whirl-ing in the breeze. Ev-'ry-where we hear the hum of bus-y hon-ey bees.

Apple Blossoms is to be freely interpreted: through the music of the first movement, moving arms and fingers express falling petals; through the second movement, children are free to dance and interpret apple blossoms blowing in the spring breezes.

3. May Baskets

Floy Adele Rossman

Long ago, the children used to make cunning little flower baskets for the first day of May. They hunted for wild flowers on the wind-swept hill tops, and for early violets under the leaves in the woods. Grandmother has often told me how she would fill the baskets with lovely flowers, and start out to distribute them in the evening before it was too dark. She would quietly hurry to the front door of a friend, hang a basket on the door knob, rap very loudly, and then rush away before she could be seen. The basket was supposed to be a gift from the "Queen of the May." It was fun to be caught, perhaps, but more fun to make the surprise.

As the music tells the story, how many baskets do you think Grandmother hung on May Day?

B. SPECIAL INSTRUMENTAL MATERIAL

1. A Little Dance

Wolfgang Mozart
Arranged by F. A. R.

VI. Listening Material

1. Morning Mood

Edvard Grieg
Arranged by F. A. R.

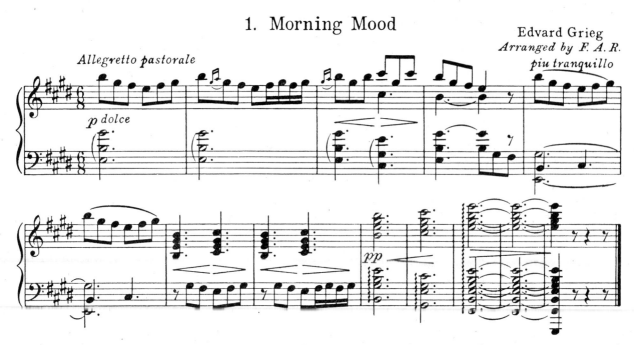

It is April. Something is happening outdoors. Is it rainy or sunny? Are there birds singing? Which of these do you think it is—robin, crow, bobolink, **bobwh**ite or sparrow?

2. All About April

J. Lilian Vandevere

298

3. Rondo-Caprice

Ludwig van Beethoven, Op. 129

4. Spring Song

Adolf Henselt, Op. 15
simplified

299

Birds

(Introductory Note. *Since the material of this and the succeeding unit is merely an amplification of the ideas discussed under Spring, and is presented separately to avoid making that discussion unwieldy, these two units will not make use of the usual sevenfold divisions.*)

I. Guiding Educational Principles

 IRDS are rightly called man's feathered friends, both because of their high degree of intelligence and because of the essential help they render to mankind. They are found in every part of the globe and adapt themselves to every sort of climate and food. Without their aid man's struggle for existence would be much more difficult.

Because of their great diversity in size, form, ability, and appearance and because of their paralleling many human traits, they easily attract and hold the interest of children. It has been said that birds "display their emotion in song and dance, parade and display, in parental love and sacrifice expressed in their nest-building labors, in their prolonged incubation and their care for and courage in defending their young."

An interest in birds awakened in a child and guided by intelligent observation and some opportunity to care for them may bring delight that will last well into adult life.

II. Musical Applications

The texts of songs about birds may deal with many of the facts discussed in the previous section. The music usually stresses the rhythms of flying and the calls or songs of the birds. These same musical ideas are often embodied in instrumental compositions.

For most of the songs which we present, the characteristic bird call upon which each is based is printed separately, both to indicate the germ of the melodic pattern of the song and to stimulate the children to listen to the notes of actual birds. A little encouragement and especially a good model such as can be found on phonograph records will lead many children to attempt to reproduce bird calls, either by singing or by whistling.

Our two instrumental numbers for listening present in conventionalized form the musical material mentioned in the opening paragraph of this section. If possible these should be supplemented by phonograph records of bird calls and music related to birds.

III. Birds Calls and Songs

1. *The Woodpecker.* 2. *Little Gray Dove.* 3. *Bob-o-Link.* 4. *The Blue Bird.* 5. *Sparrows.* 6. *The Cat Bird.* 7. *The Kingfisher.* 8. *Bob White.* 9. *The Child and the Bird.* 10. *Robin Red-Breast.* 11. *Whip-Poor-Will.* 12. *Willie Woodpecker Telegraphs.*

IV. Special Instrumental Material

A. FOR RHYTHMIC PLAY. 1. *March of the Penguins*, Rossman.

B. FOR LISTENING. 1. *The Song of the Lark*, Tchaikovski. 2. *Birdling*, Grieg.

III. BIRD CALLS AND SONGS

1. The Woodpecker

Woodpecker Patterns

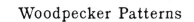

E. A.

Elizabeth Allen

Rap, tap - i - tap, tap, tap!

Rap, tap - i - tap, tap, tap!

The wood - peck - er taps on the
Come out, mis - ter bug, or I'll

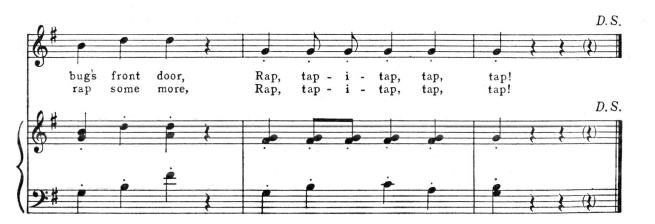

bug's front door,
rap some more,

Rap, tap - i - tap, tap, tap!
Rap, tap - i - tap, tap, tap!

D.S.

2. Little Grey Dove

3. Bobolink

4. The Bluebird

F.A.R.

Floy Adele Rossman

1. Ear - ly in the spring, We hear the blue-bird sing.
2. Hap - pi - ness he brings, On blue and love - ly wings.

Tru - ly, tru - ly, tru - ly.

5. Sparrows

H.S.

Harriet Storrs

Lightly

1. Sau - cy lit - tle spar - rows, They chat - ter all the day,
2. They are nois - y bird - ies. I won - der what they say.

(Spoken lightly in time with accompaniment).

Chit, chit, chat - ter, chit, chit, chat - ter, chit, chit, chat - ter, chat.

The catbird also has a very beautiful song of his own in early spring.

9. The Child and the Bird

Margery Armitage

Theresa Armitage

Un-der the grass, a wee bob-white Stut-ters a song while out of sight. Bob-bob-bob-white. Bob-bob-bob-white. Bob-bob-bob-white, Bob-white.

(The Child) Moth-er bird, have you a nest? (The Bird) Yes, I own a love-ly tree.

(The Child) Have you an-y ba-by birds? (The Bird) Yes, they're wait-ing now for me.

10. Robin Redbreast

A.C.W.

Angela C. Wiechard

I hear rob - in red - breast sing - ing, He sings for you, he sings for me. He sings for his ba - bies swing-ing A - way up in the tree. —

11. Whippoorwill

Whippoorwill Call

Whistle

Whip-poor-will, Whip-poor-will.

E.A.

Elizabeth Allen

Moderately fast

1. When the night is dark and still,
2. We would real - ly like to know

We can hear the whip-poor-will, Whip-poor - will, Whip-poor-
Why he sings of Wil - lie so,

will, Whip-poor - will.

306

W. W. Telegraphs

Morse Code, W   —   W   —   Musical Notation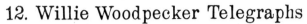
• — — / • — —

Willie Woodpecker is the bird who telegraphs. He may say to the bug "I'll eat you," or he may wire his friends, "I'll meet you," but he always signs his name, W. W.

12. Willie Woodpecker Telegraphs

F.A.R.

IV. SPECIAL INSTRUMENTAL MATERIAL

A. FOR RHYTHMIC PLAY

1. March of the Penguins

Floy Adele Rossman

1. The Song of the Lark

Peter I. Tchaikovski

2. Birdling

Edvard Grieg Op. 45, № 4

UNIT TWENTY-ONE

Insects, Bees and Butterflies

I. Guiding Educational Principles

A SIGNIFICANT educational principle maintains that not only will truth set us free, but that it will interest us even at an early age. Science teachers insist that children should be given facts instead of fancies, that the wonders of nature are as fascinating as fabricated fairy tales. Certainly many of the unnecessary fears of adults are due to false ideas acquired in childhood.

Insects are by far the largest group of living creatures — there being between five and ten million species. While the damage wrought by them is enormous, they contribute greatly to the life and health of mankind by disposing of dead vegetation and tissues, by warring upon some of their own numbers which are particularly destructive to mankind, and especially by fertilizing crops through cross-pollination. Beetles are frequently imported, as in the citrus industry of California, to take care of pests with which man could not otherwise cope.

Bees and butterflies are particularly interesting to children, the former because of their highly social and co-operative life and the latter because of the complete cycle of metamorphosis from egg to caterpillar to cocoon to butterfly. The threefold division of bees into queen or mother bee, drones, and workers is charmingly presented in the next book of this series, OUR SONGS, through the use of a musical playlet, *The Ant Reporter Interviews The Bees.*

Both the bee and the butterfly assist in cross-pollination. The bee also contributes honey and beeswax, while the beauty of the butterflies' wings is "sheer delightful waste to be enjoyed in its own high right."

II. Musical Applications

As with birds, music about insects can make use of their movements and their sounds. They move in many different ways —they walk, run, jump, glide, and swim, and even the legless kind squirm along. Children enjoy imitating the movements and sounds of various insects as these are presented in nature or in the musical material they hear. We print a few suggestions but children will usually originate others that will please them better.

III. Calls and Songs

1. *Sound of the fly.* 2. *Sound of a bee going off for honey.* 3. *Sound of a bee coming to a flower.*

4. *The Bee.* 5. *Business-Like Bee.* 6. *Song of the Bumble-Bee.* 7. *The Caterpillar's Nap.* 8. *Quite a Change.* 9. *About a Butterfly.* 10. *The Woolly Worm.* 11. *Grand Daddy Long-Legs.* 12. *The Fire-Fly.* 13. *Willie Inch-Worm.* 14. *Yellow Butterfly.* 15. *Be Careful.*

IV. Rhythmic Plays and Dramatizations

1. *Trees and Flowers.* 2. *The Elf and the Butterfly.* 3. *The Grasshopper.*

309

III. Calls and Songs

1. Sound of the fly.

Zzz- zzz- zt   Z-z-z-z-zt

2. Sound of a bee going off for honey.

Bz- z - z - z - z - z - z - z - z - z - z - zt

3. Sound of a bee coming to a flower.

Bz- z - z - z - z - z - z - z - z - z - z - z - z - zt

4. The Bee

Words and music by
Amelia Parker
six years old

Zum, zum, zum, goes the bus-y hon-ey bee. Zum, zum,

zum, as he flies from tree to tree. Zu - m, Zu - m, Zu - m, Zum.

5. Business-Like Bee

Helen Fitch

H. W. L.
Accomp. by H. F.

1. With mm _____ the hon-ey-bee will
2. With mm _____ he'd rath-er work in-

buzz. Per - haps you think that buzz and hum is all he ev-er does.
stead. He's mak-ing hon-ey ev-'ry day, for us to eat on bread.

6. Song of the Bumblebee

F.A.R.

Floy Adele Rossman

Zz - - z - - z ——

1. I like the song of the big bum-ble-bee, I
2. So fly a-long to the gay ap-ple tree, And

like him best when he's far a-way from me.
sing your song, Mis-ter Bum-ble-bum-ble-bee.

Zz - - z ——————

7. The Caterpillars' Nap

H.F.

Helen Fitch

Moderato e legato

pp

1. Slow-ly, so slow-ly the cat-er-pil-lars
2. Out from those cra-dles where cat-er-pil-lars

creep. They'll soon make a bed in a chrys-a-lis, and sleep.
lie, Some warm day in spring love-ly but-ter-flies will fly.

8. The Change

J. L.

Jane Landon

1. The cat-er-pil-lar crawls and crawls and crawls, And wrig-gles while it creeps. It wraps it-self in a chrys-a-lis, And there it sleeps and sleeps.

2. The cat-er-pil-lar wakes in ear-ly spring, When rob-in red-breast sings, And out it comes as a but-ter-fly, With love-ly col-ored wings.

9. About a Butterfly

J. L. V.

Samuel Drake
Accomp. by Gladys Pitcher

Smoothly

1. If you watch a love-ly but-ter-fly, Some love-ly sum-mer

2. Nev-er catch a love-ly but-ter-fly, Don't try to make it

day, It will spread its wings and flut-ter by, Then light-ly float a-way, a-
stay Let it spread its wings and flut-ter by, Then light-ly float a-way, a-

rit.

way, a-way, Then float a-way.

10. The Woolly Worm

F.A.R.

Floy Adele Rossman

Slowly

slowly

I'm a bus-y lit-tle wool-ly

worm, worm, worm. When I go to take a walk, I

rall.

squirm, squirm, squirm, I'm a lit-tle fuz-zy, wuz-zy, wool-ly worm!

slowly

11. Granddaddy Long-Legs

F.A.R.

Floy Adele Rossman

With dignity

Grand - dad - dy, grand - dad - dy, grand - dad - dy long - legs, Won - der where he came from, won - der where he'll go. Fun - ny lit - tle bug with his long, long, long legs, Has he an - y grand - sons? I would like to know.

12. The Firefly

H.S.

Harriet Storrs

1. I won - der where the fire - fly went
2. I won - der where he hides his lamp

when he bought his light.
when the sun is bright.

I won - der where, I won - der where, I won - der where.

D. S.

13. Willie Inch Worm

F.A.R.

F. A. R.
D.S.

Lit-tle Wil-lie Inch Worm meas-ured me to-day.
"You shall have a new {suit/dress}" so he seemed to say.

Whenever a little green inch worm is found measuring himself on any garment, it is "a sure sign" that the wearer is to have a new one.

14. Yellow Butterfly

Samuel Drake
Accomp. by Gladys Pitcher

J.L.V

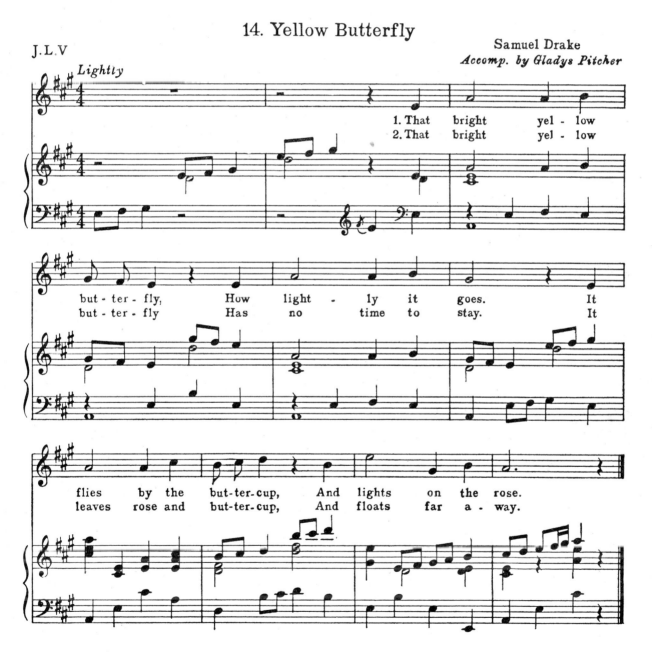

1. That bright yel-low
2. That bright yel-low

but-ter-fly, How light-ly it goes. It
but-ter-fly Has no time to stay. It

flies by the but-ter-cup, And lights on the rose.
leaves rose and but-ter-cup, And floats far a-way.

15. Be Careful

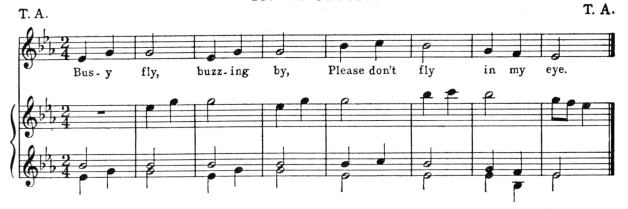

Bus-y fly, buzz-ing by, Please don't fly in my eye.

IV. RHYTHMIC PLAYS AND DRAMATIZATIONS

1. Trees and Flowers

F.A.R.

Floy Adele Rossman

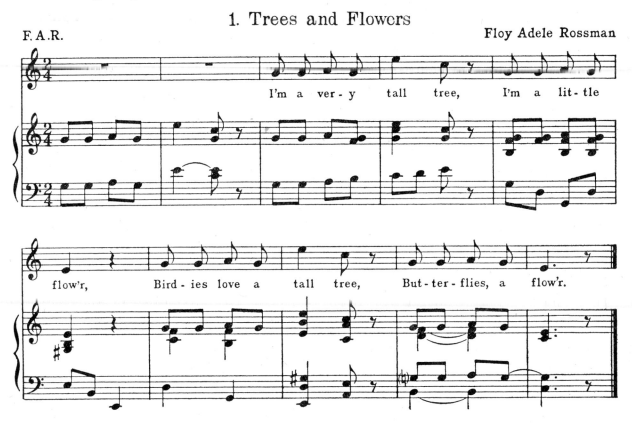

I'm a ver-y tall tree, I'm a lit-tle flow'r, Bird-ies love a tall tree, But-ter-flies, a flow'r.

Perhaps you have never seen fairies, and indeed, perhaps you have. But if a cunning little elf were chasing a lovely butterfly, can you imagine how he would leap high into the air trying to catch the beautiful wings? Listen to the music.— Can you hear the little elf run? Can you tell when he jumps so swiftly into the air? But he must soon come down again, very lightly, on his tiny feet.

Do you think he ever catches the lovely butterfly?

Try singing about the little elf's leaping high in the air,—

Up high, down, up high, down.

2. The Elf and the Butterfly

François Joseph Gossec
Arranged by F. A. R.

Allegretto

3. The Grasshopper
(Bourree)

French Folk Tune
Arranged by F. A. R.

Allegretto

The Circus, the Zoo, and Animals, Too

I. Guiding Educational Principles

FOR thousands of our children the annual arrival of the circus means the big play-day of the year. Anticipation begins with the posting of the first colorful announcements and these, on the billboards long after the great day, continue pleasant memories for months afterward. The educational significance of such an event should not be overlooked.

The color, action, and comedy of the circus are missing from the zoo — an entertainment and educational feature which, fortunately, through public and private donations, is becoming much more common in our American communities. But the zoo has not the distractions of the big tent and the blaring band which make it difficult for children to linger long enough before the animals in the cages. Moreover, in many cities the zoo houses its animals in such comfort and spaciousness, that the animals display their natural tendencies much better than in the pent-up cages of the circus.

And even in towns and villages too small for a real zoo, there are frequently modest collections where children can become acquainted with these four-legged friends in which their story books have already stimulated an interest.

II. Musical Applications

Stories and poems about animals are as old as mankind; the fables of Aesop date back to the sixth century, B. C. And just as our ancestors were not content merely to see the animals move and hear their cries, so our children demand that the animals shall display human traits and even talk our language. A favorite pastime of childhood is the imitating of animals and the assuming of their characteristics.

The calls of the vendors and barkers form an important part of the sounds of the circus. Children who have seen a circus will be able and eager to supplement our few samples.

III. Calls and Motives

A. CIRCUS CALLS. 1. *Soda-Pop!* 2. *Ice Cream.* 3. *Lemonade.* 4. *The Peanut Man.* 5. *Pop Corn.* 6. *Ice Cream Cones.* 7. *Balloons.*

B. MOTIVES FROM SONGS. 1. *Circus Time.* 2. *The Clown.* 3. *Playing Bear.* 4. *Circus Clown.* 5. *Big Brown Bear.*

Imitations of animals at the circus or zoo may easily be translated into song. For city children "zoo" is a fascinating word, and the discovery of words that sound like it has lead some to make verses and songs such as:

"I went one day to the zoo
I saw the kangaroo;
I saw a pigeon named 'Pooh'
Who had the mumps and flew."

IV. Songs

A. FOR CHILDREN TO SING. 1. *Circus Time.* 2. *The Clown.* 3. *Playing Bear.* 4. *The Lion.* 5. *The King of Beasts.* 6. *Camels.* 7. *The Hoppity Kangaroo.* 8. *The Mother Beaver's Tail.* 9. *A Monkey's Tail.*

B. FOR TEACHER TO SING TO CHILDREN. 1. *Circus Clown.* 2. Baby Kangaroo. 3. *Big Brown Bear.*

V. Rhythmic Plays and Dramatizations

1. *March*, Tchaikovski. 2. *The Circus Calliope*, Stephen C. Foster (Arr.). 3. *Grand Processional*, Italian Folk Tune (Arr.). 4. *Running Horses*, Mendelssohn. 5. *Comic Dance*, Mendelssohn. 6. Pantomime: *In the Hall of the Mountain King*, Grieg. 7. *Dainty Dancer* ("For Elise") Beethoven. 8. *Dragon Theme*, Wagner.

III. Calls and Motives

A. CIRCUS CALLS

1. Soda Pop

Ice-cold pop, So-da pop! So-da pop! Ice-cold pop!

2. Ice Cream

Ice cream! Three kinds in a box.

3. Lemonade

Buy your lem-o-nade! Five cents a glass! Lem-o-lem-o-nade Fi' cents a glass!

4. The Peanut Man

Pea-nuts! pea-nuts! Five cents a bag.

5. Pop Corn

Pop corn! Fresh but-tered pop corn! Pop corn! Pop corn!

6. Ice Cream Cones

Ice cream cones! Ice cream cones, get your nice ice cream cones!

7. Balloons

Bal-loons! Bal-loons! Buy a bal-loon! Ten cents.

B. MOTIVES FROM SONGS

1. Circus

Cir-cus time!

2. The Clown

He'll tum-ble,

3. Playing Bear

I'm a great big bear.

4. Circus Clown

Oh I'm a fun-ny cir-cus clown.

5. Big Brown Bear

Big Brown Bear!

IV. Songs

A. FOR CHILDREN TO SING

1. Circus Time

320

clown. He'll tum-ble, he'll tum-ble, he'll tum-ble, tum-ble down.
clown. They tum-ble, they tum-ble, they tum-ble, tum-ble down.

3. Playing Bear

F. M.

Frances McCollin
Accomp. by H.F.

I'm a great big bear, And be-hind that chair Is the

cave that I made my - self. And a piece of cake I am

going to take, When I crawl through the woods to the shelf.

4. The Lion

H. W. L.

Harvey Worthington Loomis

1. I went to see the li - on, His cage is made of i - ron, He brushed his hair with
2. My moth-er says they told her, When he's a lit-tle old-er, He'll be a yel-low

one big paw, And took his tail to sweep the floor. I love to see the li - on!
par-lor rug To keep our feet all warm and snug, When he's a lit - tle old - er.

5. The King of Beasts

F. A. R.

F. A. R.

With dignity

1. The Li - on called the
2. They thought it most un -

an - i - mals, And he gave them all a feast. And he
us - u - al, But they all were at a feast, So the

said,"We've come to - geth - er here, to e - lect me King of Beasts."
tall gi - raffe so dig - ni - fied, crowned the Li - on King of Beasts.

6. Camels

F.A.R.

Floy Adele Rossman

Rather slowly

Cam-els have humps and bumps and

lumps. Ev - en their heads make la - zy bumps. When - ev - er they

kneel, They grum-ble and squeal, I'm glad I don't ride on a cam-el. ___

7. The Hoppity Kangaroo

J.L.V.

J. Lilian Vandevere

1. Kan - ga - roo, kan - ga - roo,
2. Hop and hop, hop and hop,

How do you hop the way you do? Your legs are real - ly
How do you know the place to stop? When I've a chance to

won - der - ful things, I think that you must be made with springs.
vis - it the zoo, I spend all my time in watch - ing you.

8. The Mother Beaver's Tail

Frederic Manley

William Peters

Moderato

The moth-er beav-er's tail is flat, It's al-so broad and strong. Her

chil-dren, by re-mem-b'ring that, Are kept from do-ing wrong.

poco rit.   *a tempo, gaily*

9. A Monkey's Tail
(Chorus)

Frederic Manley

Arthur Bergh

Swing - ing in the jun - gles Where the ti - gers grow, ___

Watch - ing bears and pan - thers prowl - ing 'round be - low, ___

Eat - ing nuts and paw-paws while you play and swing, Oh! I think a mon-key's tail's a

ver - y hand-y thing, Oh! I think a mon-key's tail's a ver - y hand-y thing.

1. Circus Clown

A.C.W.

Angela C. Wiechard

Oh, I'm a fun-ny cir-cus clown, My nose is paint-ed red, I walk up-on my hands and knees, I stand up-on my head, And when at last I tum-ble down, and bump my head in play, I quick-ly get right up a-gain, and run the oth-er way.

2. Baby Kangaroo

S.B.

Stephene Blake

Slowly and lightly

When the moth-er kan-ga-roo Takes her ba-by rid-ing,—— She hides him safe a-

326

3. Big Brown Bear

A.C.W.

Angela C. Wiechard

way from view, But we know where he's hid - ing.

With stump-y tail of fur so fun - ny, Big Brown Bear! He

likes the woods and likes his hon - ey, Big Brown Bear! It's

one foot up and one foot down, Thats the way he walks a - round. He

takes a nap when it's warm and sun - ny, Big Brown Bear!

V. Rhythmic Plays and Dramatizations

1. March

Peter I. Tchaikovski

2. The Circus Calliope

Stephen O. Foster
Arranged

3. Grand Processional

Italian Folk Song
Arranged by Charles Repper

4. Running Horses

Felix Mendelssohn
Tarentella

Presto

5. Comic Dance

Felix Mendelssohn
Arranged by F.A.R.

Allegro molto

6. Pantomine
(In the Hall of the Mountain King)

Edvard Grieg, Op.46

Alla marcia e molto marcato

sempre staccato

R.H. repeat an octave higher

R. H. repeat an octave higher

R.H. repeat an octave higher

7. Dainty Dancer

Ludwig van Beethoven
Für Elise

Poco moto

8. Dragon Theme

Richard Wagner
In Act Two of *Siegfried*

Slowly

UNIT TWENTY-THREE

Traveling

I. Guiding Educational Principles

AT the close of the school year, we present a unit which is pointed toward vacation activities. Traveling is to be considered as involving different kinds of locomotion, what is seen while these take place, and what the child, himself, can do, during and after his travel. In each phase self-activity and a measure of original self-expression is to be expected. If the work of the year has been successful, the child should be alert to the sights, sounds, and movements of the world and should be eager to identify himself with them to the extent of expressing them physically.

Not only should he be eager to imitate sounds and movements but he should realize that, since each of us is a little different, the imitations of the same thing by different children may vary greatly. He has learned a valuable lesson when he is able to compare his accomplishments with those of his mates, not in terms of one "beating" another, but in terms of interesting differences, thus leading to enjoyment of what his mates do. Such an attitude moreover leads to the storing up of impressions that may be shared with his companions and members of his family when opportunities arise

II. Musical Applications

In the sounds which vehicles make and in the movements and calls and songs of the workers, there are many musical motives. Some of these are worth while for the child to imitate for their own sake and some he may develop into somewhat longer musical compositions.

Since, in imagination at least, travel may take the child into foreign lands, we also present some music which suggests other countries. A happy extension of the idea of traveling in imagination by using the music of foreign countries might be worked out by recalling and reviewing the folk material in other units.

III. Calls and Motives

A. CALLS: 1. *Tug Boat.* 2. *Steamer.* 3. *Bell Buoy.*

B. MOTIVES FROM SONGS: 1. *To Market.* 2. *Skipping Along.* 3. *My Scooter.* 4. *The Auto.* 5. *The Ferry Boat.* 6. *The Sailor Lad.* 7 (a and b). *Click-i-ty Clack.* 8. *The Song of the Roller Skates.*

IV. Songs

A. FOR CHILDREN TO SING. 1. *To Market.* 2. *Skipping Along.* 3. *China Boy Walks.* 4. *My Scooter.* 5. *The Auto.* 6. *The Ferry Boat.* 7. *The Sailor Lad.* 8. *Click-i-ty Clack.* 9. *A Boat Trip.* 10. *Merrily We Roll Along.*

B. FOR TEACHER TO SING TO CHILDREN. 1. *The Song of the Roller Skates.* 2. *The Bus.* 3. *The Aeroplane.*

V. Rhythmic Plays and Dramatizations

1. *Song of the Sailors.* 2. *The Merry-Go-Round.* 3. *Dancing in the Country.* 4. *Country Dance,* Reinecke.

The children should be helped to regard these as examples of rhythmic actions they may meet and should be encouraged to suggest others.

VI. Listening Material

1. *Echoes from the Theater,* Schumann. 2. *Gipsies,* Reinhold. Treat this material in much the same way as that suggested under V.

VII. Rhythm Band

Many effective compositions for this activity are included in this unit, such as: IV-A 3, 4, 7, 8; IV-B 1; V 1, 2, 3, 4; VI 1, 2.

III. CALLS AND MOTIVES

A. CALLS

1. Tug-boat

Chug - a - chug - a, chug - a - chug - a, chug - a - chug - a - chug.

2. Steamer

I'm on my **way,** toot - toot - toot - too._____

3. Bell Buoy

I've a song, a song, song, Go a - long a - long - long.

B. MOTIVES FROM SONGS

1. To Market

To mar - ket, to mar - ket.

2. Skipping Along

Hip - pi - ty hop.

3. My Scooter

My scoot-er scoots.

4. The Auto

Honk! Honk! Honk! Honk!

5. The Ferry Boat

Chug - a, chug - a, chug!

6. The Sailor Lad

Hi - ho the sail - or!

7a. Clickity Clack

Toot - toot!_____ toot - toot!_____

7b.

A click - i - ty clack.

8. The Song of the Roller Skates

Roll a - long, Roll a - long.

IV. SONGS

A. FOR CHILDREN TO SING

1. To Market

English Folk Tune
Accomp. by P.W.D.

Gaily

To mar - ket, to mar - ket, to buy a pen - ny bun. Home a - gain, home a - gain, mar - ket is done.

2. Skipping Along

A.C.W.

Angela C. Wiechard

Happily

I'm skip-ping a - long with Cous - in Jack, Hip - pi - ty hop, Hip - pi - ty hop, Just o - ver to grand-ma's house and back, Hip - pi - ty, hip - pi - ty hop.

3. China Boy Walks

H.S.

Harriet Storrs

Chi - na boy go walk - ing down the
Nev - er ride when Chi - na boy is

1. street.

2. strong, with stur - dy feet.

4. My Scooter

F. A. R.

Floy Adele Rossman

Allegro

My scoot-er scoots, and scoots, and scoots, I give it a push and a-way it shoots. It's here, and there, and ev-'ry where. I feel like a bird as my scoot-er scoots!

sempre staccato

5. The Auto

F. A. R.

F. A. R.

Allegro

Honk! Honk! The au-to calls
Honk! Honk! I've man-y a

sauc-i-ly, Honk! Honk! Move out of my way!
mile to go. Honk! Honk! Move out of my way. Honk! Honk!

6. The Ferry Boat

F.A.R.

Floy Adele Rossman

Allegro

1. "I must hur-ry, I must hur-ry," Chugs the bus-y
2. "Do not wor-ry, I will hur-ry," Chugs the bus-y

fer-ry boat. Chug-a, chug-a, chug-a, chug-a, chug-a, chug-a chug!
fer-ry boat.

7. The Sailor Lad

S.B.

Stephene Blake

Hi - ho, the sail-orl I would be a

sail-or, A jol-ly sing-ing sail-or lad,

1. Sail-ing out to sea.
2. Com-ing home from sea.

8. Clickity Clack

A. E.

Ann Engels

Moderato

A click-i-ty clack, a click-i-ty clack, The train is hum-ming a-long the track, A click-i-ty clack, a click-i-ty clack, I hur-ry a-way, I'll soon come back. Toot-toot___ toot-toot___ toot-toot___ toot-toot.___

poco a poco accel.

accel.

9. A Boat Trip

H. F.

Helen Fitch

1. Stand on the deck of a boat,___
2. Stand on the deck of a boat,___

Look at the wa-ter be - low.____ You can't see a sign of a
Say - ing good-bye to the shore.____ You tra - vel a - long on the

road or a track, But the boat knows where to go.____
top of the waves, Till you're back in port once more ____

10. Merrily We Roll Along

American Folk Tune
Accomp. by P. W. D.

Mer - ri-ly we roll a - long, roll a - long,

roll a - long. Mer - ri-ly we roll a - long, O'er the deep blue sea

337

1. The Song of the Roller Skates

E. A.

Elizabeth Allen

My rol-ler skates hum a song so gay, "Roll a-

long, roll a-long, roll a-long. We trav-el far on the

road to-day, Roll a-long, roll a-long, roll a-long. Roll a-

long, roll a-long, roll a-long, roll a-long, roll a-long!"

2. The Bus

F.A.R.

Floy Adele Rossman

The bus runs down the street with a roar, and it stops, with a jerk. The peo-ple rush out through the door when it stops, with a jerk! I like to watch the world go by as we ride through the town. And when we reach our av-e-nue we stop, with a jerk.

3. The Aeroplane

S.B.

Stephene Blake

1. High o-ver head, the aer - o-plane Is fly-ing a-long through wind and rain, With a
2. Swift-ly a - way, the aer - o-plane Is fly-ing a-long through wind and rain,

rush_____ and a roar_____ and a pr-r-r-r _____

(may be spoken with trilled R)

V. Rhythmic Plays and Dramatizations

1. Song of the Sailors

18th Century French Folk Tune
Arranged by F. A. R.

If the muscles of the children are sufficiently co-ordinated so that they can step on one foot and swing the other in a slow march, the arm movements of a Hornpipe dance may be added.

On the first beat of the measure, the left hand is swung to the front of the waist line and the right hand to the small of the back. The hands alternate position, and come to rest on the third beat of the measure.

As the children gain muscular control, there is a delightful abandon to the swing of the music.

2. The Merry-Go-Round

Floy Adele Rossman

3. Dancing in the Country

Polish Folk **Tune**
Arranged by F.A.R.

4. Country Dance

Carl Reinecke

VI. LISTENING MATERIAL

1. Echoes from the Theater

Robert Schumann

2. Gipsies

Hugo Reinhold, Op. 39

The Three Bears and Goldilocks

THIS, like the other units, should help the children see old ideas in a new light, develop their musical and dramatic powers, and extend the spirit of co-operation. These values which appear naturally if the little opera is used only for class room purposes, need not and should not disappear if it develops into a public performance. To that end we make the following suggestions:

I. Without making any reference to a musical setting, the teacher, with such help as the children can give, may narrate a well-known version of the *Three Bears*.

II. The teacher may read dramatically the version written by Margery Armitage.

III. The children should be encouraged to dramatize this libretto using sections of the music such as these, suggested by the teacher.

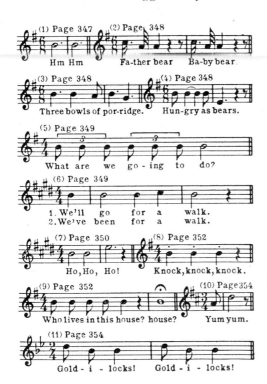

IV. The children may now be told that this version has been made into a little opera, which may now be played and sung.

V. If a complete presentation of the opera is to be given, the preparation should extend over a sufficiently long time to allow the children to become well acquainted with it. The children should be encouraged to devise or to suggest action which will fit with the music. The printed directions should serve as a guide in evaluating what the children suggest, rather than as exact commands governing the various characters.

VI. Special mention should be made of the music which is printed in smaller or lighter type to indicate that it is optional. Such notes in the piano part may be omitted if they interfere with smooth playing. In the voice parts, they may be sung (there are occasionally children who can do this) or spoken either freely or in the rhythm indicated by the notes. It is desirable at all times to have the appropriate portions of the text at least begin at the times indicated by the music. This will not be difficult to accomplish if the children, especially the four main characters, hear the music often enough before they try to fit in their sung or spoken text.

VII. The dance at the close may be devised by the children after they have heard the music played several times—in much the same way that they devise movements for their rhythmic plays. They will soon notice that the music of the dance is made up chiefly of the marching song of the bears and the skipping theme of Goldilocks—both themes being modified to fit into a very regular country dance form. The suggestions printed at the end may be modified to suit individual requirements.

THE THREE BEARS AND GOLDILOCKS

by MARGERY ARMITAGE

(MOTHER BEAR *is shown filling the bowls with porridge, and placing the chairs She is moving about clumsily, and humming in a gruff voice. Goes to door at back of stage and calls*)

M.B.   Father Bear! Baby Bear! Come to breakfast!

FATHER BEAR and BABY BEAR come lumbering in, all three go to table, singing)

> Three bowls of porridge
> Three little chairs;
> Hurrah! For we all
> Are as hungry as BEARS!

(*The* BEARS *sit down together, and all take a heaping spoonful of porridge, together. Much sputtering!*)

F.B.   (*growls*)   My porridge is too hot!

M.B.   (*gruffly*)   My porridge is too hot!

B.B.   (*squeaks*)   My porridge is too hot!

ALL   What are we going to do?

(*They put their paws to foreheads in deep thought. They jump up shouting*)
We'll go for a walk! (*They march around in single file, singing*)

> We'll go for a walk
> While it cools, Ho! Ho!
> While the porridge is cooling
> A-walking, we'll go!
> We'll go for a walk while the porridge
>   cools!
> A-walking we'll go, Ho! Ho!

(*As the* BEARS *walk off stage, the stage is empty for a few moments when a voice is heard outside.*)

GOLDILOCKS (*off stage*)

What a darling little house   I wonder who lives in it? I'll soon find out

SONG (*off stage*)

GOLD.   Knock! Knock! Knock!
CHO.   (*echo*) Knock! Knock! Knock!
GOLD.   Who lives here?
CHO.   (*echo*) Who lives here?
GOLD.   Knock! Knock! Knock!
CHO.   (*echo*) Knock! Knock! Knock!
GOLD.   Who lives in this house?
CHO.   (*echo*) House!

GOLD.   Knock! Knock! Knock!
CHO.   Knock! Knock! Knock!
GOLD.   No one home?
CHO.   No one home!
GOLD.   Knock! Knock! Knock!
CHO.   Knock! Knock! Knock!
GOLD.   In I come!
CHO.   Come!

(GOLDILOCKS *enters from the outside. She tiptoes around, looking here and there and then sees the table. She runs over to it and claps her hands, saying*)

GOLDILOCKS

Goody! Goody! Porridge! And what cunning little chairs! (*She sits on F.B.'s chair and tastes his porridge.*) OUCH! This is too hard! and the porridge is too hot! (*She sits on M.B.'s chair and tastes her porridge.*) UGH! This is too soft, and the porridge is too cold! (*She runs to B.B.'s chair and sits on it, but it breaks down.*) This chair was just right. I'm sorry I broke it. But the porridge is perfect, I'll eat it all up. Yum, Yum!

(*While she is eating, the* CHORUS *sings*)

Goldilocks, Goldilocks!
Shame upon you!
What will the poor little Baby Bear do!
He will go hungry! That's what he'll do!
Goldilocks, Goldilocks!
SHAME — ON — YOU!

(*When* GOLDILOCKS *finishes, she stretches and rubs her eyes and says*)

GOLD. I'm sleepy! I think I shall take a nap!

(*Exit into the other room.*)

(*The* THREE BEARS *come in, singing as they go up to the table*)

We've been for a walk
Down the old Bear Track.
Twice as hungry as bears,
We now come back.

(*They start to sit down.*)

F.B. (*growls*) Some one has been sitting in my chair!

M.B. (*gruffly*) Some one has been sitting in MY chair!

B.B. (*squeaks*) My porridge is gone
There isn't a sup!
And my little chair
Is broken up!

(*The* BEARS *look at each other in amazement.*)

ALL We'll find out who is in this house!

(*Exeunt to bedroom.*)

(*Off stage*)

F.B. (*growls*) Some one has been in MY bed!

M.B. (*gruffly*) Some one has been in MY bed!

B.B. (*squeaks*) Some one has been in MY bed!
And HERE SHE IS!

(*Much growling, squeaking, screaming etc off stage; then* GOLDILOCKS *runs from the bed room, screaming, with the* BEARS *in clumsy pursuit. She runs out of the cottage. The* BEARS *stand at the door looking out, crowding each other to get a look. They turn and come up stage.*)

F.B. (*growls*) We gave HER a scare!

M.B. (*wistfully*) I wish I had her bright golden hair!

B.B. (*cooly*) My! She is pretty!
So I don't care
If SHE ate my porridge
And broke my chair!

ALL What are we to do for breakfast?

(*Again they put their paws to their foreheads in deep thought, then jump up and down.*)

ALL We'll go for a walk!

(*They march clumsily around in single file, singing*)

A-walking we'll go! Hi! Hi! Hi!
Ho! Ho!

Our porridge is spoiled and we have no bread

But berries for breakfast we'll use instead!

A-walking we'll go! Hi! Hi! Hi!
Ho! Ho!
Hi! Ho! Hi! Ho!

(*They march out.*)

CURTAIN

To the twins and the four others
THE THREE BEARS AND GOLDILOCKS
Children's Opera in One Act

Libretto by
Margery Armitage

Music by
Peter W. Dykema

CHARACTERS IN THE OPERA

FATHER BEAR
MOTHER BEAR
BABY BEAR
GOLDILOCKS
UNSEEN CHORUS (*dressed as Teddy Bears if they appear*)

STAGE PROPERTIES

Three chairs
Three bowls
One table

All three pause ALL

What are we go-ing to do? What are we go-ing to do?

One after another THE BEARS *put their paws to their foreheads and, to the rhythm of the music, gently scratch, in deep thought. They hum as they scratch.*

BABY BEAR· MOTHER BEAR FATHER BEAR

Hm Hm Hm

Slowly and getting slower

ALL

Seized with an idea, they first think it over quietly, p *slowly.*

Then they jump up together f *and sing brightly.*

Clumsily but happily in easy march tempo

Hm We'll go for a walk, we'll go for a walk.

f *twice as fast as before*

THE THREE BEARS *march around* mf *the room and sing in single file.*

We'll go for a walk while it cools, Ho! Ho! While the

mf

They go out ***f* THE UNSEEN CHORUS *sings.***

walk while the por - ridge cools. A - walk - ing they'll go. Ho, Ho, Ho,

Ho!

growing softer like an echo

hold back

(Music of GOLDILOCKS *outside, approaching and examining the home of* THE BEARS.*)*

Gracefully, not fast

staccato

p a tempo

mf

GOLDILOCKS *(outside) singing or speaking:*
"What a dar-ling lit-tle house!"

*Notes printed in small type are optional for playing or singing.

"I won-der who lives in it?"   "I'll soon find out."

hold back

GOLDILOCKS (*outside*) UNSEEN ECHO-CHORUS GOLDILOCKS   CHORUS

mf Moderato   *p*   *mf*   *p*

Knock, knock, knock,   knock, knock, knock,   Who lives here?   Who lives here?
Knock, knock, knock,   knock, knock, knock,   No one home,   No one home.

mf Moderato   *p*   *mf*   *p*

p a tempo   *pp*   *p*   *pp*

GOLDILOCKS   CHORUS   GOLDILOCKS   CHORUS

mf   *pp*   *mf*   *p*

Knock, knock, knock,   knock, knock, knock,   Who lives in this house?   house?
Knock, knock, knock,   knock, knock, knock,   In   I   come,   come.

mf   *pp*   *pp* hold back

p   *pp*   *a little slower*

GOLDILOCKS *enters from outside. She tiptoes around, looking here and there, and then sees the tables.*

a little faster

f   *rit.*

352

sor-ry I broke it. But the por-ridge is per-fect, I'll eat it all up, Yum, Yum."

Mischievously

She sits on the MOTHER BEAR'S *chair,*
and eats BABY BEAR'S *porridge.*

UNSEEN CHORUS

Gold-i-locks! Gold-i-locks! Shame up-

hold back a little

mf a tempo

on you. What will the poor lit-tle Ba-by Bear do? He will go hun-gry,

that's what he'll do! Gold-i-locks! Gold-i-locks! SHAME ON YOU!___

357

have no bread, But ber - ries for break - fast we'll use in -

stead. A - walk - ing we'll go, Ho, Ho, Ho, Ho, Ho, Ho, Hi,

*Ending A.
BEARS *go out.*
Omit, if Ending B is used
Curtain

Ho, Hi, Ho! _____

Ending B.
BEARS *march out.*
THE UNSEEN CHORUS *dressed as teddy bears enter*
(see suggestions printed on page 80).

Ho! _____

Ⓐ *Moderato*

rit.

* *Note:* If a livelier ending is desired, these three final measures, marked Ending A, may be omitted and the succeeding music for the entrance of THE UNSEEN CHORUS and a dance, marked Ending B, may be substituted.

Gaily, but not too fast

Repeat section Ⓑ if desired   Ⓒ

Ⓓ   Ⓔ

hold back

SUGGESTIONS FOR THE DANCE

We present some general suggestions rather than specific directions so that each teacher may feel free to devise movements appropriate to the powers of her children. Moreover, the children themselves will often have ideas which may be used effectively.

As indicated by the encircled letters printed in the music, there are six divisions or sections in the music, each of which may be temporarily isolated for rehearsal purposes. Three of them, B, C, and E, each sixteen measures in length, constitute the main dance sections.   B is danced by the Teddy Bears alone; C by the Three Bears and Goldilocks; and E by everybody.   We now present a complete picture of the dance.

(A) (4 measures)— The Three Bears having gone out, the Unseen Chorus, dressed as teddy bears, enter, with stiff but still light movements, for a frolic.   They arrange themselves in a circle, either single or double, with all facing the same way or half to the right and half to the left.

(B) (16 measures)— They move about the circle for eight measures and then return, going slowly enough so as to lift their feet high. If desired, they may, during some of the music, such as the final few measures, pat their large padded hands with each other.   If this movement is too short to include all the necessary action, the sixteen measures may be repeated.   At the end of it, say during the last four measures, Goldilocks may enter with the Three Bears lumbering after her.

(C) (16 measures)— The Three Bears and Goldilocks, at the front of the stage, dance by themselves, Goldilocks weaving in and out around the Three Bears.

(D) (4 measures)— The Three Bears and Goldilocks take their places in a large circle formed by everyone on the stage.   The Father Bear and the Mother Bear join hands at a spot opposite where the Baby Bear and Goldilocks join hands.

(E) (16 measures)— The entire group now repeat the actions used in Section B.

(F) (2 measures)— The group form a tableau and the curtain closes.

Classified Index

Alphabetical Index

ALPHABETICAL INDEX (CONTINUED)

ALPHABETICAL INDEX (continued)

ALPHABETICAL INDEX (CONTINUED)

ALPHABETICAL INDEX (CONTINUED)